THE FALLEN SKY

Medical Consequences of Thermonuclear War

Edited for *PHYSICIANS FOR SOCIAL RESPONSIBILITY* by

PAUL ARONOW, FRANK R. ERVIN, M.D., and *VICTOR W. SIDEL*, M.D.

$1.50

The Fallen Sky

MEDICAL CONSEQUENCES OF THERMONUCLEAR WAR

The Fallen Sky

MEDICAL CONSEQUENCES OF
THERMONUCLEAR WAR

Edited for Physicians for Social Responsibility by
SAUL ARONOW, PH.D., FRANK R. ERVIN, M.D., and
VICTOR W. SIDEL, M.D.

HILL AND WANG · NEW YORK

FIRST EDITION AUGUST 1963

The editors would like to thank the Houghton Mifflin Company for the use of Dr. Bentley Glass's article, "The Biology of Nuclear War," which appears in *Problems of Disarmament;* Mr. Gerard Piel for permission to use "The Illusion of Civil Defense," which was delivered as a lecture before the Commonwealth Club of San Francisco; and the *Bulletin of the Atomic Scientists,* published by the Educational Foundation for Nuclear Science, 935 East 60th Street, Chicago 37, Illinois, for permission to reprint Mr. Piel's article, which appeared in their February 1962 issue.

Manufactured in the United States of America by
The Colonial Press Inc., Clinton, Massachusetts

"—Earthquake, Wind, and Fire" *

THE EDITOR OF THE NEW ENGLAND
JOURNAL OF MEDICINE

A SPATE of material has been published on the subject of thermonuclear war and its consequences, and the resultant confusion is
understandable. Not only does the magnitude of the destructive
force increase with each technical advance in this form of annihilation, but the pattern of distribution of a potential enemy's attack is
quite unpredictable, regardless of the logical assumptions. The
physical effects of strikes of various intensity are reasonably cal-
culable, but where they might actually occur and how to protect
against them is still a matter of guesswork, despite the information
and advice that have poured forth through every conceivable chan-
nel as well as from those official agencies whose business it is to
advise the public to the best of their ability.

The dangers of fallout seem to have caught the popular fancy
even more than the infinitely greater destructiveness of blast and
fire storm, and the matter of shelters has presented an especially
confusing problem. On the whole, people seem to be going about
their business as usual; habit, as William James expressed it, is "the
enormous fly-wheel of society, its most precious conservative
agent."

Perhaps the most logical attitude that one can take is to view the
known facts on which assumptions can be currently based at any
given period in the technical progress of the arms race and try to

* Editorial, *New England Journal of Medicine,* Vol. 266, p. 1174, May
31, 1962.

assess the predictable results of an attack. These do not permit any high degree of optimism regarding the rate of survival in a target area, and it is obvious that shelter building can represent only a gamble against unknown odds.

The special articles on the medical aspects of thermonuclear war published elsewhere in the *Journal* are based on the best available factual evidence and the assumptions that can be made on the basis of this evidence. The purpose of the symposium is to establish the part that the surviving physicians should play in the event of an attack, since they would have special professional duties to perform, as is usual in times of disaster.

The most important function of the physician, however, relates to prevention. So very little can be done in the area in which a bomb or a series of bombs has been exploded that the employment of every reasonable means to prevent such a catastrophe becomes the concern of everyone, and not least the physician.

It is no longer a matter of a nation's hiding from the blast or fleeing from it, but of preventing it. This is not to be accomplished unilaterally, by abjection, but by convincing all the participants of the folly of the competition, and showing determined leadership in finding a way out. As Whittier wrote:

> Breathe through the heats of our desire
> Thy coolness and Thy balm;
> Let sense be dumb, let flesh retire;
> Speak through the earth-quake, wind, and fire,
> O still, small voice of calm.

Contents

Illustrations

Introduction

DESCRIPTIONS of a thermonuclear attack and its sequelae are limited by the availability of pertinent data and by the need to rely upon a host of uncertain assumptions. The limitations of the data result in part from governmental classification and in part from the happy fact that few nuclear weapons (and no thermonuclear weapons) have been exploded over major cities. Information resulting from coral-reef blasts may not be applicable to cities of concrete, steel, glass, and macadam. The major assumptions, however, lie in the political and military sphere. It is obvious that there is no certain way of predicting the nature of a thermonuclear attack on the United States. Since no single system of defense can meet all the possible conditions of attack, there is no sure way of predicting the efficacy or futility of a given civil-defense program. Numerous models of thermonuclear war have been presented to the public in recent years. The models range from massive single strikes against missile bases to repeated multimegaton saturation bombing of cities. In the former, significant protection might be provided for individuals in cities by adequate shelters against radioactive fallout. In the latter, no system of shelters would spare the people of the urban and industrial centers from blast and fire.

This is an age in which the scientific and technological revolution has provided military forces with an exponential growth in the power of weapons. The fission bombs dropped over Hiroshima and Nagasaki represented a thousandfold increase in destructiveness as compared to their chemical predecessors; the development of fusion bombs represents a further thousandfold multiplication. Guided missiles, antimissile missiles, neutron bombs, and manned space platforms all influence the validity of plans for civilian protection. The rapid rate of arms development has been reflected in the changing and at times contradictory civil defense program. The public seeks the facts and a coherent policy. Yet the magnitude of the spiraling arms race, the complexities of the cold war, and the ever increasing size of the government create a broadening gulf between citizen and decision-making process.

Any formulation of the subject of thermonuclear war must state its assumptions regarding the type of attack. The assumptions chosen by the authors of the following papers are those of the Joint Congressional Committee on Atomic Energy (the Holifield Committee). The Committee heard testimony from many authoritative sources and arrived at a hypothetical attack, which its members, in 1959, considered a "realistic possibility." Of course, the attack may be less severe; on the other hand, in the light of recent thermonuclear-weapon development, the Committee report may be an underestimate. The 1446-megaton attack on missile bases and urban-industrial complexes of the United States envisaged by the Committee is probably an underestimate in the era of the 100-megaton high-altitude explosion, tidal-wave and fire storm production, and rapid advances in missile technology.

The hypothetical attack postulated by the Holifield Committee is obviously only one of many possible patterns of destruction. This very uncertainty makes the planning of a rational "defense" extremely difficult, if not impossible. In a "logical" war as described by our game theorists, all weapons might be directed at military targets. If the interpretation of P.M.S. Blackett and others is correct that the Soviet Union has relied entirely on a limited number of deterrent missiles, these few would of necessity have cities as targets.

Aside from this uncertainty, it is clear that the attack of 1446 megatons and the use of maximum 10-megaton weapons suggested in 1959 is trivial by today's standards. Without considering the theoretically possible increases in human destruction made possible by such refinements as sodium-oxide or cobalt-60 bombs (*cf.* W. H. Clark, "Chemical and Thermonuclear Explosives," *Bull. Atomic Scientists,* Nov. '61, pp. 356-360), 50-megaton bombs now exist and may be deliverable. In general, the effects of bombs larger than the 10 MT described here can be calculated by the following rules:

a. The radius of blast effect is multiplied by the cube root of the increase in size—for example, a 50-megaton blast would increase blast destruction by approximately 1.7 times. The decrease in perimeter in relation to the involved area of course magnifies the problems of rescue and salvage out of proportion to this simple scale factor.

b. The radius of thermal effect increases as the square root of the increase in bomb size, 2.25 times for a 50-megaton bomb. This effect is reduced somewhat by the fact that heat is produced over a longer time in large explosions so that more total calories are required to ignite objects or burn flesh. The radius of effect is of course increased by increasing the height of the explosion above the ground.

c. The amount of radiation released is increased directly with the bomb size. This assumes construction similar to the 10-megaton bomb the Holifield Committee referred to, since, within limits, more or less fallout can be designed. We have used the assumption of ½ fission for this article since this is the lowest official fission content in current devices. The fallout radiation is dependent on how much the fireball involves the earth's surface; that is, an air burst produces little or no fallout.

The first group of articles in this book was originally written by a group of physicians for the *New England Journal of Medicine* to describe for their fellow physicians the biological, physical, and psychological consequences of a thermonuclear attack. Since so much has appeared in technical journals and in the lay press on these subjects, why should physicians pay special attention to the problem? The answer is clear. No single group is as deeply involved in and committed to the survival of mankind. No group is as accustomed to the labor of applying practical solutions to threats to life. Physicians are also aware that intelligent therapy depends on accurate diagnosis and a realistic appraisal of the disease. It was therefore felt that physicians, in their roles as protectors of the health of the community and advisors to their patients, must become fully informed.

The physicians who wrote these articles are members of Physicians for Social Responsibility, an organization formed to increase the awareness among physicians and the public of the technical and ethical implications of the arms race and of modern warfare. The statement of purpose of this group says in part:

We believe that the physician's response to this challenge must stem from his dual role as scientist and as clinician. As a scientist he is a custodian of technical information, trained in the analysis of complex problems, and experienced in the objective presentation of data. It is the physician's responsibility as scientist to study the medical consequences of nuclear testing, of attack by chemical or biological weapons, and of thermonuclear war. It is the physician's further responsibility as scientist to share his knowledge with the public, in order to make possible rational discussion and informed decision-making by the community.

But the physician's responsibility goes beyond his role as scientist. He is also a clinician, often forced to make decisions affecting human life while relying on data which admit of no certain conclusions. He is an active participant, not only an impartial supplier of information.

In the nuclear age the physician's commitment to the health of his patients obliges him to examine certain key propositions:

a. that the armaments race and the continued testing of nuclear weapons increase the danger of war;

b. that planning by our own or any other government which tolerates the risk of nuclear war but promises an effective defense constitutes a vast and scientifically unsupportable gamble with human life;

c. that while the survival of some individuals may be possible no modern society can survive a full-scale thermonuclear attack.

These propositions lead to a conclusion familiar to the physician: there are situations in which prevention is the only effective therapy. The physician charged with responsibility for the lives of his patients and the health of his community must begin to explore a new area of preventive medicine, the prevention of thermonuclear war.

The aims of Physicians for Social Responsibility are to provide for the medical community and the general public the scientific data on which political decisions must in part be based; to alert physicians to the dangerous implications of the arms race; to involve physicians in serious exploration of peaceful alternatives; and to develop support for programs promoting effective disarmament and peace.

The response to these articles by the readers of the *New England Journal of Medicine* has been extremely gratifying. At the suggestion of Mr. Arthur W. Wang of Hill and Wang, Inc., and with the permission of the *Journal,* the articles have been slightly modified for a broader audience and two articles have been added. "The Illusion of Civil Defense" is a speech given by Gerard Piel, publisher of *Scientific American,* at the Commonwealth Club in San Francisco in November 1961; "The Biology of Nuclear War" by Dr. Bentley Glass, Professor of Biology at The Johns Hopkins

University and a member of the National Academy of Sciences, was presented to the National Association of Biology Teachers in December 1961 and was published in the October 1962 issue of *The American Biology Teacher*.

It is not the intent of the authors to provide a comprehensive plan for survival in the face of a thermonuclear Armageddon; it should be clear from the articles that there is no rational basis for such plans. It is their intent, rather, to demonstrate the magnitude of the threat that thermonuclear war presents. It is hoped that readers will carefully consider the implications of these articles for their roles as citizens in a nuclear age and will be stimulated to play a greater part in the search for peaceful alternatives to thermonuclear war.

The Fallen Sky

MEDICAL CONSEQUENCES OF THERMONUCLEAR WAR

Human and Ecologic Effects in Massachusetts of an Assumed Thermonuclear Attack on the United States

FRANK R. ERVIN, M.D., JON B. GLAZIER, M.D.,
SAUL ARONOW, PH.D., DAVID NATHAN, M.D.,
ROBERT COLEMAN, M.D., NICHOLAS C. AVERY, M.D.,
STEPHEN SHOHET, M.D., and CAVIN P. LEEMAN, M.D.

IN RECENT MONTHS public anxiety and confusion over the possibility and consequences of thermonuclear war have been increased and deepened by extensive (and often conflicting) publicity in newspapers and popular magazines, federal and local government announcements, and commercial advertising concerning shelter programs. Many people, uncertain about what course to follow, have turned to physicians to provide expert information. These requests for evaluation and plans have ranged from consideration of immediate fallout effects to the optimal design of fallout shelters, the long-term prospects of blood dycrasias,* and the suggestion of modification of medical-school curricula to meet the needs of a postholocaust practice.

Many physicians, in turn, have had no opportunity to find and study the data on which any scientific and realistic appraisal of the medical consequences of thermonuclear attack must be based. Although numerous medical publications have dealt with one or

* See Appendix II, A Glossary of Medical Terms.

1

another aspect of the problem with varying degrees of specificity, their conclusions have been conflicting; this reflects differences in the interpretation of data or—more often—differing but unstated underlying assumptions concerning the size, nature, and characteristics of the hypothesized assault.

It appears to be useful, therefore, to review the nature of a clearly defined and specified thermonuclear attack on the United States and some of its short-term human and ecologic consequences in a given area, in particular, metropolitan Boston and other targets in Massachusetts. Careless extension of these observations to other areas of the nation is not warranted, but the same methods of analysis will yield similar findings for other states and regions.

Although many pertinent facts are unknown or have been classified, enough information is available to permit such a review. Information has been presented in official governmental publications, including *Biological and Environmental Effects of Nuclear War*,[1] *The Effects of Nuclear Weapons*[2] and *Some Effects of Ionizing Radiation on Human Beings*.[3] In addition, a recent monograph by Stonier[4] has summarized this information within a broad context.

Statement of the Problem*

The hearings before the Radiation Subcommittee of the Joint Congressional Committee on Atomic Energy (the Holifield Committee) in 1959 were devoted in large part to an analysis of a "limited" attack of 1446 megatons on selected targets in the United States.[1] We have used this attack as the basis for our discussion. It should be noted that such attack, considered realistic in 1959, could be greatly exceeded in the light of recent weapons developments.†

The attack is assumed to occur in late fall after harvest, in fair weather, during the working day, and to provide twenty to thirty minutes' warning, equivalent to intercontinental-ballistic-missile flight time from the Soviet Union to the eastern United States. The further assumption is made that there is only one strike, so that fallout, fire, and other effects decay proportionately with time. The

* See Appendix I, A Glossary of Radiation Terminology.
† See Appendix III, Orders of Magnitude.

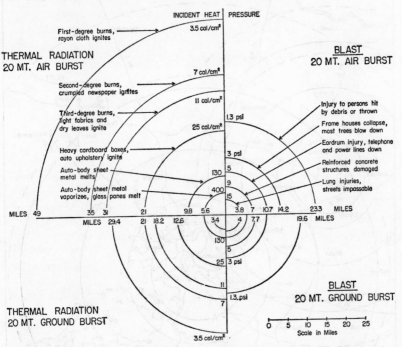

FIGURE 1. *Effects of the Detonation of a 20-Megaton Fusion Bomb as a Function of Distance from Ground Zero.*

Upper right quadrant: blast effect at indicated distances for an air burst, in terms of pounds per square inch of overpressure and corresponding physical effects. Lower right quadrant: similar relations, but at reduced distances for a ground burst. Upper left quadrant: thermal effects at indicated distances for an air burst, in terms of calories per square centimeter of incident radiation and corresponding physical effects. Lower left quadrant: similar relations, but at reduced distances for a ground burst.

general availability of individual or community fallout shelters, meeting current Office of Civil and Defense Mobilization recommendations, will be assumed. The attack pattern assigns 10 weapons, totaling 56 megatons, to Massachusetts.

Because of the complexities of overlapping effects from many target areas, we shall limit the detailed examination to the results of ground-level explosions of 20 megatons on downtown Boston* and 8 megatons on nearby Bedford Air Base. In addition, we shall

* The pattern presented at the hearings before the Holifield Committee includes two 10-megaton bombs on Boston, but it seems reasonable to assume a single 20-megaton burst.

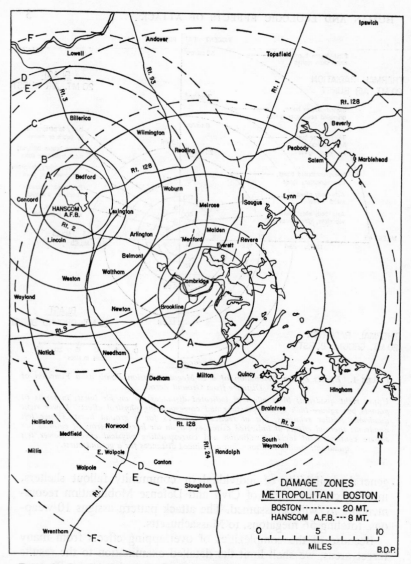

FIGURE 2. *Detailed Map of the Overlapping Thermal and Blast Effects of the Boston and Bedford Explosions, as Detailed in the Text.*

The concentric circles represent the blast effects, as described in the text for Boston and corresponding effects for Bedford at a 4-mile radius from the target (A), at a 6-mile radius from the target (B), at a 10-mile radius from the target (C) and at a 15-mile radius from the target (D), as well as the distance at which third-degree burns would be produced on exposed flesh (E) and that at which second-degree burns would be produced and fuel, leaves, cloth, paper, and so forth would ignite (F)—this is therefore the extent of a possible fire storm.

refer to the total pattern of this attack on southern New England to clarify the magnitude of the problems of planning in Massachusetts. The physical consequences of such an attack include damage from blast, heat, and radioactive fallout; these will be treated separately.

Direct Blast Effects

The assumed 20-megaton ground blast (Fig. 1) would excavate a crater 250 to 300 feet deep and half a mile in diameter, heaping rubble over the surrounding area. (An air burst would produce no crater but would almost double the area destroyed.) The area of total destruction, in which even the most heavily reinforced-concrete structures and deep blast shelters would be demolished, would have a radius of *4 miles*.[2] This would encompass the area from the ocean to Watertown, and from Everett to Dorchester (Fig. 2), thus including most of the medical facilities and personnel in the Boston area.

In a *6-mile* radius, including Newton, Arlington, Melrose, and Milton, all frame or brick buildings and any basement shelters would be totally destroyed. Lung damage from blast alone would produce total casualties of any exposed population, as would the heat, or the instantaneous radiation.

At *10 miles,* roughly to circumferential Route 128, reinforced-concrete buildings would be seriously damaged but partially reparable, whereas all other structures would be demolished. Deep blast shelters would be effective protection in this zone, but fallout shelters would be useless.

To a radius of *15 miles,* including Saugus, Lexington, Weston, Natick, and Quincy, all frame buildings would be damaged beyond repair and shelters under them compromised. Serious damage would be done in this area by flying objects carried by shock waves. In an exposed population, casualties from this factor are estimated to run as high as 15 per cent.[4]

Some damage to construction would extend to much greater distances from the hypocenter, overlapping the effects of other explosions (Fig. 3). Medical facilities as far away from Boston as Emerson Hospital in Concord would be seriously jeopardized by blast alone.

Casualties from blast result from three hazards. The first of these, primary effects of blast-produced overpressures, include eardrum

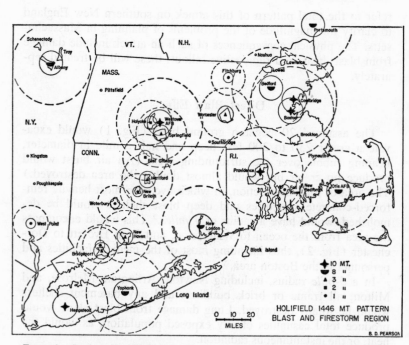

FIGURE 3. *Southern New England Target Area of the Hypothetical Nuclear Attack, with Bomb Sizes Assumed at Specific Military and Industrial Targets Indicated in the Legend. Circles indicate radii of possible destruction, not including additive effects of overlap. Inner solid circles are areas of severe blast damage to strong structures and complete collapse of frame houses. Outer dashed circles represent limits of some mechanical damage, ignition of fires in easily combustible materials and possible extent of fire storm.*

and lung rupture, although persons exposed to these (20 to 50 pounds per square inch) are more likely to be killed by heat or falling debris. The next consists of secondary effects from damage after collapse of buildings and the impact of penetrating and non-penetrating missiles energized by blast pressures, winds, and gravity. Many of these objects, including flying glass and masonry, would be a hazard as far away as 18 miles. There is therefore a risk for persons remaining outside buildings, even if they lie flat in protected gullies. A forewarned population, however, may have taken cover inside buildings or in basement shelters. For these persons, the risk may be increased by structural collapse and falling debris. The final hazard comprises tertiary effects, involving injuries occurring as a consequence of displacement of human beings by blast, shock, and wind. Such physical displacement could injure a 160-pound man at a distance of 20 miles from target, though—for persons caught in the open at this distance—thermal damage would pose more of a threat than the blast hazards.

Thermal Effects

Thermal energy is released by the bomb in two pulses. The first, a brief ultraviolet flash, is not a hazard, but the following infrared pulse, containing nearly 35 per cent of the bomb's energy, would produce burns on exposed persons and ignite inflammable material for many miles (Fig. 2). Up to 21 miles from the 20-megaton surface burst a person would have second-degree burns of all exposed skin, and his clothing and other easily inflammable material in the environment would ignite. As far as 40 miles away, a reflex glance at the fireball would produce blindness by retinal burning. (After the Marshall Island tests, small animals 345 miles distant were found with focal retinal burns.[2]) The distances to which these thermal effects extend would be increased by explosion in the air rather than on the ground, or decreased by the presence of fog or smoke.

It has been estimated that typical American cities contain 5 to 25 potential ignition points per acre; a dry countryside might contain many more.[2] As the bomb explodes, a huge pressure wave initially traveling at a speed greater than that of sound spreads out from the center of the explosion, followed by wind at speeds transiently exceeding 1000 miles per hour. The wind creates a low-pressure area as it moves outward, and surrounding air rushes in, fanning the many fires started by the thermal radiation and initial blast damage. Thus, in a radius of 16 to 21 miles around the Boston target the immediate ignition of houses, foliage, oil tanks, gasoline, and so forth would create a huge fire storm initially swept toward the center at 150 to 200 miles per hour and maintained by lower-velocity fire-produced winds. Such a fire storm developing after a series of conventional air raids on Hamburg in 1943 produced temperatures estimated at 800°C. (1472°F.).[5] Days after the raid, as some shelters were opened, enough heat was found to have remained so that the influx of oxygen caused the entire shelter to burst into flames. Deaths inside shelters in Hamburg were described as due to heat stroke, dehydrating effects of intense heat, and carbon monoxide poisoning.

TABLE 1.   *Casualties and Property Damage in Three Massachusetts Cities Resulting from Blast and Fire Storms after a Thermonuclear Attack.*

AREA	EFFECTS OF BLAST ALONE		THERMAL & BLAST EFFECTS	
	TOTAL DESTRUC- TION OF BUILD- INGS, INCLUD- ING DEEP BLAST SHELTERS	FATALITIES	FIRE-STORM & BLAST CASUAL- TIES (ASSUMING NO SELF-CON- TAINED BLAST SHELTERS)	FATALITIES
Boston	5.0-mi. radius	739,000	15.0-mi. radius	2,240,000
Springfield	3.15 mi.	174,000	5.6 mi.	250,000
Worcester	2.65 mi.	187,000	4.9 mi.	205,000
Totals		1,100,000		2,695,000

The Hamburg (and Leipzig) experience is particularly germane in relation to the shelter problem, for as Caidin[5] points out, only those who *fled* their shelters in the early stages of fire had any hope of reaching safety. Thus, huddling in a home shelter, particularly one without a self-contained air supply, might well be fatal if a fire storm developed overhead. Near the periphery of the fire storm, deep blast shelters would provide adequate thermal insulation, but only if supplied with sufficient oxygen to allow complete isolation from the external atmosphere for several days.

From the foregoing data it is possible to make a numerical estimate of the casualties from blast and heat that would occur in the Boston area, assuming that every person would be in a fallout shelter at the time of the attack and thus not subject to radiation. In the 4-mile radius of total destruction, the number of Boston residents killed outright would be at least 739,000 (*Census Handbook,* 1950), which does not include the commuter population. Within the 16-mile radius of the fire storm, assuming that no significant number of people is located in adequate deep blast shelters, an additional 1,501,000 persons would be killed, raising total deaths in the Boston area to 2,240,000. More distant persons who survived the instantaneous effects might need treatment for missile or blast injury, burns of second or third degree, including retinal damage, and conceivably for heat stroke or carbon monoxide poisoning. Similar estimates of casualties after the bomb drops shown in Figure 3 in the Springfield and Worcester areas are included in Table 1 and indicate that these three bursts alone are capable of destroying three fifths of the total population of Massachusetts.

Radiation Effects

The preceding analyses demonstrate that blast and fire damage, rather than radiation, constitute the major hazards for large areas surrounding the hypocenter. Radiation, however, would create a problem for persons beyond the range of immediate destruction. The initial burst (5 per cent of bomb energy) of neutrons and high-energy gamma rays is locally lethal but limited to the blast-destroyed area. Some materials, activated by this initial neutron flux, would contribute to later fallout. The 10 per cent of total bomb energy that goes into radioactive fission products is distributed in two parts. From a ground burst, some 20 per cent is made up of very fine particles, which are carried into the stratosphere with the mushroom cloud. These travel with upper-level winds and descend over months or years as global fallout of long-lived isotopes. The remaining 80 per cent of both short-lived and long-lived radionuclides begins to descend within minutes and continues for forty-eight hours, the rate of descent depending on particle size. It should be emphasized that this pattern would not be true for an air burst, as at Hiroshima or Nagasaki, where there was little or no local fallout.

PHYSICAL DISTRIBUTION OF FALLOUT

For purposes of calculation an idealized fallout pattern has been assumed in official publications.[2] Our calculations are based upon the method outlined in this reference, but assume a wind of 40 miles per hour, as stated at the Holifield Committee hearings.[1] Winds of lesser velocity would produce more intense fallout over a smaller area.

One assumes a "ground-zero circle" of about 8 miles, which includes the fallout of heavier particles from the initial column and mushroom cloud. This material descends within the first hour after detonation, producing radiation that is unimportant since in this area there would be few survivors of blast and heat. The lighter particles require a longer time to come down and are displaced downwind, forming first an ellipse and ultimately a cigar-shaped figure. The best available estimate of the range of particle sizes in areas of hazardous fallout is 50 to 400 microns.[2] A 340-micron particle requires three quarters of an hour, and a 75-micron particle

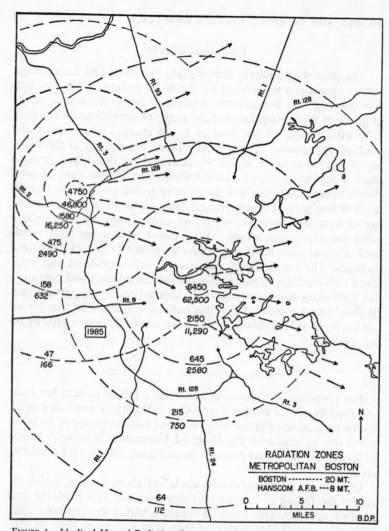

FIGURE 4. *Idealized Map of Radiation Contours for the Boston and Bedford Explosions Alone, Indicating on Each Contour Line the Reference One-Hour Dose Rate in Roentgens per Hour at 3 Feet above Ground Level.*

The adjacent larger number represents the integrated dose for two weeks after the explosion, on the assumption that fallout begins in the outermost region at one hour and in the innermost immediately. The one boxed number represents average cumulative doses produced by the overlap of fallout fields. One can calculate such levels for any other region on the map by adding the indicated doses. This map emphasizes both the importance of the overlapping effects in assessing radiation and the possibility of extreme variations in levels in adjacent areas. Construction of such a map for New England (not shown) indicated initial levels of at least 10,000 to 12,000 per hour for most of Southern New England, the highest levels being present in Eastern Massachusetts, Rhode Island and Connecticut.

sixteen hours to descend from 80,000 feet. With a 40-mile-per-hour wind, the 340-micron particle would be blown about 22 miles from ground zero, and the 75-micron particle about 560 miles. Thus, they would arrive at angles of 5° and 0.1° from the horizontal respectively and could enter an open shelter window or door.

It is generally assumed that 80 per cent of the total radiation due to local fallout would descend in the first forty-eight hours. From the idealized pattern, an area of contamination of 4000 square miles would follow a 20-megaton burst on Boston, such that an unshielded person at the edge of this area would receive 450 rem* (an LD_{50}, or lethal for 50 per cent of the population, dose) in forty-eight hours. However, the smooth contours described above are produced by idealized wind patterns, which do not exist in nature. For example, in the 1954 tests at one location 100 miles from the hypocenter, 2300 roentgens were received in thirty-six hours. At another location, 25 miles from the first and 115 miles from the hypocenter, only 150 roentgens were received.[2]

The assumption that 80 per cent of the radioactive material produced will return to earth as local fallout has also been questioned. It might be much less. On the other hand, all information on local fallout has been obtained from kiloton bursts on silicate, or from megaton bursts on coral sand. The fallout resulting from a surface burst in a city of concrete and steel might possess quite different properties.

CALCULATION OF RADIATION LEVELS

Various methods have been proposed for the determination of the pattern of radioactivity in the area surrounding a bomb burst. One must first estimate the decay rates of the deposited radioactive material. Next, one must decide whether to assume a uniform field of radiation over the whole area, or to allow (as we have done in Figure 4) for wind effects, which would result in radiation contours. Ralph Lapp[1] examined the decay rates suggested in testimony before the Holifield Committee; these yielded various estimates of gamma radiation, ranging from 2400 r to 7000 r per hour at one hour after detonation. On the basis of actual field data, he proposed a 4000-r-per-hour rate, uniformly distributed over a 4000-square-mile area, as a model of the radiation levels. His assumptions include decay rates which yield the dose schedule

* See Appendix I.

TABLE 2. *Cumulative Gamma-Ray Dose at 3 Feet above Ground Level at Intervals after Detonation of a 20-Megaton Bomb, Assuming Uniform Fallout over 4,000 Square Miles.*[1]

INTERVAL	DOSE DURING INTERVAL	CUMULATIVE DOSE FROM 1 HR. AFTER DETONATION
	roentgens	*roentgens*
1-2 hr.	2,500	2,500
2-3 hr.	1,250	3,750
3-4 hr.	800	4,550
4-5 hr.	550	5,100
5-10 hr.	1,500	6,600
10-24 hr.	1,550	8,150
2d day	950	9,100
3d day	500	9,600
4th day	300	9,900
5th day	225	10,125
6th day	175	10,300
7th day	120	10,420
2d wk.	535	10,955
3d wk.	285	11,240
4th wk.	140	11,380
2d mo.	220	11,600
3d mo.	100	11,700
4th mo.	60	11,760
5th mo.	40	11,800
6th mo.	25	11,825
6th-12th mo.	60	11,885
2d yr.	20	11,905
3d yr.	6	11,911
4th yr.	3	11,914

shown in Table 2 for a single 20-megaton ground-level explosion.

An individual shelter with 20 inches of concrete (giving a protection factor of 250, as usually suggested by the OCDM) would reduce the cumulative two-week dose from 10,955 r to 45 r (assuming that one remained continuously inside the shelter). One-half time outside the shelter during the next two weeks would add 215 r; three-quarter time during the remainder of the year would add 380 r. This total of 640 r in one year is probably compatible with individual human survival, but would have long-term genetic and somatic effects.

These figures, as we have indicated, are based on the assumption of a uniformly contaminated field. Contour maps allowing for wind effects make calculations more difficult but probably more realistic. For example, radiation levels near the hypocenter may be three to

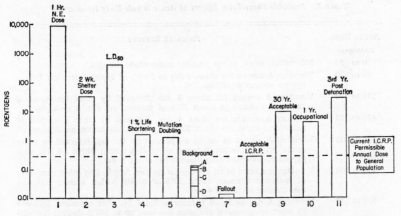

FIGURE 5. *Comparison of Radiation Levels.*

Note that the scale is logarithmic so that, for example, bar 1 is 100,000 times or 5 orders of magnitude greater than bar 6. (See Appendix III for discussion of this point.) The bars are identified as follows (note some differences in the time scales involved): initial (one-hour) dose rate for Southern New England (1), under the conditions specified in the text, corrected for additional fallout arriving from New York State alone; cumulative dose (2) received by a person continuously in a shelter with a 250 protection factor for two weeks after detonation of a single 20-megaton weapon (use of the data in bar 1 would increase this by 2.5 times); estimated lethal dose for half an exposed population (3); estimated level that shortens life expectancy by 1 per cent, based on animal experiments (4); estimated level that doubles mutation frequency in mammalian germ cells (5); natural background activity for American population (6), composed of man-made radiation, such as x-rays, luminous watch dials and television screens (A), internal emitters—K^{40}, C^{14}, Ra^{226} and so forth (B), gamma rays from granite—radium, thorium and so forth (C) and cosmic rays at sea level (D); estimated accumulated global fallout from testing through 1961 (7); annual dose suggested by the International Commission on Radiologic Protection as the "maximum permissible" for the general population from all sources (8); "maximum permissible" total cumulative dose (thirty years) suggested by the Commission for the general population (9); "maximum permissible" total cumulative dose (one year) suggested by the Commission for occupational exposure (10); and annual dose during the third-year post attack at the level indicated in bar 1 (11).

five times the average, whereas the peripheral areas may be much less contaminated. Figure 4 demonstrates such a pattern for the Boston area. The hourly rates indicated are for one hour after detonation. The cumulative doses are proportional to the values shown in Table 2.

MEDICAL CONSEQUENCES OF RADIATION

Consideration of radiation problems in an exposed population must include initial exposure before shelter is reached, low-level accumulation in the shelter and later emergence into a radioactive environment (Fig. 5).

TABLE 3. *Probable Short-Term Effects of Acute Whole-Body Irradiation.*[2]

ACUTE DOSE	PROBABLE EFFECTS
roentgens	
0 to 50	No obvious effect, except possibly minor blood changes.
80 to 120	Vomiting & nausea for about 1 day in 5-10% of exposed persons; fatigue but no serious disability.
130 to 170	Vomiting & nausea for about 1 day, followed by other symptoms of radiation sickness in about 25% of persons; no deaths anticipated.
180 to 220	Vomiting & nausea for about 1 day, followed by other symptoms of radiation sickness in about 50% of persons; no deaths anticipated.
270 to 330	Vomiting & nausea in nearly all persons on 1st day, followed by other symptoms of radiation sickness; about 20% deaths within 2-6 wk. after exposure; survivors convalescent for about 3 mo.
400 to 500	Vomiting & nausea in all persons on 1st day, followed by other symptoms of radiation sickness; about 50% of deaths within 1 mo.; survivors convalescent for about 6 mo.
550 to 750	Vomiting & nausea in all persons within 4 hr. after exposure, followed by other symptoms of radiation sickness; up to 100% deaths; few survivors convalescent for about 6 mo.
1000	Vomiting & nausea in all persons within 1-2 hr.; probably no survivors.
5000	Incapacitation almost immediately; all persons dead within 1 wk.

To estimate medical consequences one must first clarify the levels at which radiation damage occurs. Most official documents give estimates in terms of the LD_{50}. At this level, 400 to 500 r, given as a short-term dose, would permit the survival of 50 per cent of a healthy young adult population. From a medical point of view, however, even much lower levels (about 225 r) would take the lives of some persons, particularly the young, the old, those with pre-existing disease and those with blast or burn injuries. Furthermore, the choice of 400 to 500 r as the LD_{50} ignores genetic and long-term somatic effects (for example, leukemia) of these high-level exposures. Levels of even 50 to 100 r would increase the late incidence of cancer and leukemia[6,7] and double the spontaneous gene mutation rate.[3,8] Aronow, in Appendix I, compares these dose rates with dose rates from more familiar sources, such as natural background, diagnostic x-rays and so forth.

Short-term effects of fallout may be divided into three classes: whole-body radiation injury produced by penetrating radiation; superficial burns produced by soft radiation (beta and low-energy gamma); and injury produced by deposition of radionuclides in specific organs. Each of these types of radiation injury may produce both acute signs and later chronic manifestations.

Table 3, adapted from Glasstone,[2] summarizes the short-term effects of acute whole-body irradiation.

Whole-body doses of several thousand roentgens produce a "central nervous system syndrome" with inevitable death in hours or days, preceded by hyperexcitability, ataxia, respiratory distress, and intermittent stupor.

Doses of 1500 r may produce only a "gastrointestinal syndrome" before death, with nausea, vomiting, diarrhea, and necrosis of intestinal mucosa. Although death usually occurs in the first week, these cases would contribute to the immediate medical-emergency problem. (The following article by Sidel and his associates surveys this problem.)

Doses below 1500 r result in a gastrointestinal syndrome of decreasing severity, so that at levels of 200 r only mild radiation sickness occurs in most adults and is characterized by hair loss, nausea, diarrhea, malaise and weakness, delayed healing, and lowered resistance to infection. Granulocytopenia, anemia and thrombocytopenia may produce hypoxia and purpura, and increase the possibility of infection.* In Japan (where the air bursts produced little fallout) deaths from infection were most prevalent in the second and third weeks, and from hemorrhagic phenomena in the third to sixth weeks, although some radiation deaths occurred in the seventh week and later.

The overlap of responses and the similarity of presenting symptoms in persons who have been lethally irradiated and those who have received much smaller doses would create major diagnostic problems in the postattack period. Few, if any, survivors would know whether they have received 1000 r or 100 r. In attempting, for practical reasons, to classify irradiated persons into three groups whose survival is improbable, possible, or probable, one would have to rely on very broad symptomatic rules of thumb in the absence of adequate laboratory facilities, trained technicians, and the opportunity to follow survivors systematically for several weeks or more. The following general descriptions apply to the various categories of irradiated survivors:

Group 1 (survival improbable). If vomiting occurs promptly and continues, followed rapidly by prostration, diarrhea, anorexia, and fever, the prognosis is grave. Even intensive therapy may be ineffectual.

Group 2 (survival possible). These patients show early vomiting of short duration, followed by a period of apparent well-being.

* See Appendix II.

Lymphocytes are depressed and remain so for months, neutrophils are depressed and drop to zero at seven to nine days, remaining below 1000 per cubic millimeter during the second week. Platelets may reach their lowest level after two weeks, with external evidence of bleeding in two to four weeks. In the most severely irradiated of this group the latent period may be one to three weeks, with little evidence of injury other than fatigue. At the end of this time epilation, purpura, diarrhea, and infections will appear, followed, in the absence of vigorous treatment, by high mortality. If such persons enter shelters after their initial radiation exposure, a serious management problem would be created during the next several weeks.

Group 3 (survival probable). These persons may or may not have had fleeting nausea on the first day. If there are no further symptoms, hematopoietic changes are the best indicator of exposure. Lymphocytes reach low levels within forty-eight hours. The granulocytes may become depressed from the second to the seventh week or even later. Platelets reach the lowest count on about the thirtieth day. Medical problems center around decreased immune mechanisms and impaired healing.

OTHER IMMEDIATE SYMPTOMS

Although superficial burns from beta radiation do not contribute to the hematologic depression they increase the possibility of infection and create other problems. From twenty-four to forty-eight hours after exposure, a fourth of the 64 exposed Marshall Islanders experienced itching and burning of the skin; a few had burning of the eyes and tearing. These symptoms subsided in two days but within two weeks after exposure epilation and skin lesions appeared. Early itching, burning, and slight pain were associated with the lesions. Deeper lesions produced more severe pain, and foot lesions were particularly incapacitating. No constitutional symptoms accompanied these lesions, and they healed within seven to ten days.[3]

A more serious problem might well be the impaired healing of minor injuries in persons with sublethal radiation. The mean lethal dose for many cell types is 100 r; thus, not only hematopoietic defenses but also general healing processes are impaired at this dose level. As pointed out above, many, if not all, survivors would receive doses of this level in the hypothetical attack. Malnutrition, excessive fatigue, and emotional stress would also contribute to recovery problems. Patients requiring regular insulin, digitalis, cortisone, and so forth would have additional difficulties. It seems likely that major medical problems during the first few weeks would arise out of this combination of burns or injury and impaired healing and failure of immune mechanisms.

Internal absorption of fallout would not be a serious immediate hazard and will be considered a long-term problem. A possible exception might be the inhalation of fine particles by a population in shelters, with consequent pulmonary fibrosis and radiation pneumonitis.

The task of the medical profession in dealing with all these problems, and with such further complications as loss of medical facilities and personnel, is discussed in the following article.

DELAYED EFFECTS

It is difficult to quantitate the effects of residual radiation, since many of the short-lived fission products have decayed significantly by three to six months. The residual activity is the sum of these remaining levels plus those of longer lived nuclides that have decayed less. The pattern of fallout for much of southern New England, including that deposited from distant detonations, would provide a residue of 0.5 to 1.0 r per hour at three months.[1] By the second year after detonation, levels would be slowly decaying from about 0.01 r per hour so that a constantly exposed person would get 90 r per year, which is compatible with individual survival. Much of this long-term residue is beta emitting; furthermore, it weathers and is buried in soil, increasing the difficulty of making a realistic estimate. Many of the elements that comprise the long-term residue (as pointed out in Appendix I) are physiologically significant and tend to concentrate in selected body organs. Although this residual radioactivity is compatible with human survival, its effects would create an unpredictable hazard. The effects include: increased incidence of leukemia and other neoplasia; increased degenerative disease; accelerated aging and decreased life-span; increased incidence of congenital malformations, stillbirths, neonatal deaths, and feeblemindedness; decreased fertility; and increased incidence of cataracts.

A sensitive indicator of these biologic effects is the developing embryo. A striking aspect of this problem, considering the radiation resistance of mature nerve cells, is the susceptibility of developing neural tissue. Many cells become morphologically necrotic in less than four hours after 40 r to the whole body of mother or newborn infant.[9] In Hiroshima many cases of microcephaly and an increased incidence of mental deficiency appeared in children who had been four months *in utero* at the time of the bombing.[10] Furthermore, half the substantial number of mentally defective children born in the postattack period were from mothers who had major immediate radiation exposure in the range of only 200 to 300 r. The history of abnormal termination of gestation in 45 of 177 pregnant Nagasaki survivors illustrates the dose dependency of embryo damage. The terminated pregnancies included all 19 within 1.8 miles of hypocenter, 15 of 20 between 1.8 and 11.2 miles and 11 of 138 beyond that.[10]

Effects such as these would reach important dimensions within months of the explosion. Other longer-range biologic effects will not be examined in detail, since there is little experimental information about the phenomena of delayed response.

The profoundly altered ecology of involved areas would also be of major importance, even after attack of only 1446 megatons. In many areas fire would consume the forest cover and result in severe flooding during spring thaws, lack of water retention in the drier areas, and the creation of extensive dust bowls.[1] Flowering plants and young trees are extremely sensitive to radiation, and would be affected by radiation as well as by fire, flood, and drought.

Moreover, short-term and long-term radiation effects of fallout might be expected to disrupt the balance normally maintained in the plant and animal world. Mammals and birds are highly sensitive to radiation; insects are extremely resistant (for example, cockroaches are not appreciably damaged by gamma radiation in the range of 400,000 r, which is a thousand times the LD_{50} for man).[11] Bacteria are similarly very resistant to radiation although mutation rates are increased—for example, only 10 per cent of an *Escherichia coli* population is killed by 20,000 r of gamma radiation. Viruses and fungi are even more resistant.

The longer-term survival of human populations after this ecologic upheaval would be precarious. Even assuming an intact social structure and the maintenance of a functioning work force, agriculture, particularly domestic animals, would be all but destroyed. Before malnutrition became a major medical concern, however, the threat of epidemic infectious disease would be raised by the fact that bacteria, fungi, viruses, and insects would survive the effects of radiation. The ultimate size of these populations in the absence of challenge by their natural enemies is difficult to estimate.

Summary

This article examines the short-term human and ecologic consequences in Massachusetts, and in particular in metropolitan Boston, of the "limited" thermonuclear attack on the United States postulated by the Holifield Committee report of 1959. This assigns 10 weapons totaling 56 megatons to Massachusetts. Damage would result from blast, heat, and radioactive fallout.

A 20-megaton ground burst on downtown Boston would seriously damage reinforced-concrete buildings to a distance of 10 miles, roughly to circumferential Route 128, and demolish all other structures.

Within a circle of a radius of 16 to 21 miles second-degree burns would be produced, and clothing, houses, foliage, gasoline, and so forth would ignite, producing a fire storm. Human survival in this area would be practically impossible, and an estimated 2,240,000 deaths would occur in metropolitan Boston from blast and heat alone.

Beyond the area consumed by fire, many persons would be exposed to lethal doses of radiation from local fallout. For some of these persons, fallout shelters could reduce the cumulative dose of radioactivity to levels compatible with survival, provided immediate entry into shelters was achieved and occupancy of the shelters maintained for the necessary several weeks. For many persons access to shelters would be made more difficult by blindness produced instantly by retinal burning. Many sheltered survivors would be subject to acute radiation sickness and to the long-term somatic and genetic effects of radiation.

Acute whole-body irradiation produces a variety of clinical syndromes, largely dependent on the dose of radiation absorbed. The similarity of presenting symptoms in persons who have been lethally irradiated and those who have received much smaller doses would create major diagnostic problems in the postattack period. Sublethal irradiation would increase the morbidity and mortality from pre-existing disease and from blast injuries, burns, and infections. Long-term effects of radiation due to fallout would include increased incidence of neoplasia, stillbirths, congenital malformations, and cataracts.

Serious ecologic problems would result from thermal destruction of forests and widespread lethal irradiation of mammals and birds, accompanied by relative sparing of bacteria, fungi, viruses, and insects, all of which are highly resistant to radiation.

The authors are indebted for the painstaking and thoughtful art work of Mr. Bradford Pearson, as well as for his critical commentary.

References

1. United States Congress, Joint Committee on Atomic Energy. *Biological and Environmental Effects of Nuclear War: Summary analysis of hearings, June 22-26, 1959.* 58 pp. Washington, D. C.: Government Printing Office, 1959.
*2. United States Armed Forces Special Weapons Project. *The Effects of Nuclear Weapons.* Edited by S. Glasstone. 579 pp. Washington, D. C.: Government Printing Office, 1957. (Pamphlet 39-3.)
3. United States Atomic Energy Commission. *Some Effects of Ionizing Radiation on Human Beings: A report on the Marshallese and Americans accidentally exposed to radiation from fallout and a discussion of radiation injury in the human being.* Edited by E. P. Cronkite, V. P. Bond, and C. L. Dunham. 106 pp. Washington, D. C.: Government Printing Office, 1956. (AFC-TID 5358.)
4. Stonier, T. Anticipated biological and environmental effects of detonating 20 megaton weapon on Columbus Circle. In *Effects of Thermonuclear War.* Prepared by Scientists Committee for Radiation Information. New York City, 1961.
5. Caidin, M. *The Night That Hamburg Died.* 158 pp. New York: Ballantine, 1960.
6. Cronkite, E. P., Moloney, W., and Bond, V. P. Radiation leukemogenesis: analysis of problems. *Am. J. Med. 28*:673-682, 1960.
7. Court Brown, W. M. Radiation induced leukemia in man with particular reference to dose-response relationship. *J. Chronic Dis. 18*:113-122, 1958.
8. Carter, T. C. Radiation exposure: credit and debit. *Lancet 1*:217, 1960.
9. Hicks, S. P. Effects of radiation on development of nervous system. Presented at International Congress of Neurology, Brussels, Belgium, July 25, 1957.
10. Warkany, J., and Kalter, H. Congenital malformations. *New Eng. J. Med. 265*:993-1001 and 1046-1052, 1961.
11. Glass, Bentley. "The Biology of Nuclear War." See page 74 in this book.

* N. B. Recent publication of this volume brought up to date—1962.

The Physician's Role in the Postattack Period

VICTOR W. SIDEL, M.D., H. JACK GEIGER, M.D.,
and BERNARD LOWN, M.D.

MANY MONOGRAPHS and articles[1-8] have been written to acquaint physicians with the medical problems that might follow a thermonuclear attack on this nation. Often, these articles rely on experience with previous disasters—for example, the New England hurricane of 1938, the Cocoanut Grove fire of 1942, the Texas City explosion of 1947, the fire bombing of Hamburg in 1943, and especially the nuclear bombing of Hiroshima and Nagasaki in August, 1945.[9]

To reason from these models to thermonuclear war, however, is to make the assumption that the problems of H-bomb warfare will be quantitatively greater, but qualitatively similar to those of these earlier disasters. This usually unstated assumption implies that since we have survived other catastrophes we will survive now— under any circumstances—if only we plan carefully enough. An illustrative example is the recent report by the Official Committee on Disaster Medical Care,[10] which calls on physicians to promote sound planning for handling of mass casualties, to encourage the population to engage in survival training, and to "lend assurance that a successful recovery from mass attack is possible."

The present article examines some of the medical effects of a thermonuclear attack for a defined geographic area, the state of Massachusetts. It demonstrates that thermonuclear war will differ in size and nature from anything in previous experience (and parallels with past disasters are therefore often inapplicable) and considers the implications for disaster planning.

A thermonuclear attack poses a series of questions for physicians. How many persons will be killed outright? How many will be fatally injured? How many will be injured, but survive? Similarly, how many physicians will be killed or injured? How many hospital beds will be destroyed, and how many will remain intact? Will any necessary medical supplies—drugs, plasma, blood, dressings, instruments, and the like—be left? And where will physicians, patients, beds, and supplies be in relation to one another? The answers depend, however, on still other questions. What will be the type, timing, magnitude, and distribution of the attack—or, more bluntly, how many bombs will there be? Will they be fission or fusion or both? Where will they fall? Will the attack occur in daylight or at night? Will the weather be clear or hazy, moist or dry, windy or calm? Will there be warning time? How accurate will delivery be? Will there be one strike or more? These are not rhetorical questions; each has a quantitatively measurable effect on the results of thermonuclear attack, and the total pattern of medical consequences is a function of the answers to all the questions.

Thus, there are so many variables and so many imponderables in the complex equation of thermonuclear war that one can reach almost any conclusion by choosing appropriate assumptions. The primary responsibility of the physician to the medical community and to the public, therefore, is neither to offer sweeping and uncritical reassurances nor to cry doom, but rather to define and study the consequences of a specific and possible pattern of attack.

We have based our report on the findings of the Joint Committee on Atomic Energy of the United States Congress (the Holifield Committee).[11] This scientifically detailed study has become the standard reference for those writing on the subject. In the course of official hearings in 1959 on the biologic and environmental effects of nuclear war, the Committee hypothesized an enemy attack on the United States totaling 1446 megatons. It was assumed that 263 weapons would be employed, directed at 224 targets, of which 71 were cities and industrial centers. Ten weapons of 56 megatons were "assigned" to Massachusetts.

In view of the development of over 50-megaton weapons and rapid improvements in missile capacities since 1959, there is reason to believe that this estimate is, by now, conservative.

TABLE 1. *Casualties in Metropolitan Boston and Massachusetts after a 56-Megaton Attack.*

TARGET AREA	NO. OF PEOPLE IN ATTACKED AREA*	NO. KILLED ON 1ST DAY	NO. FATALLY INJURED	NO. SURVIVING INJURED	NO. UNINJURED
Boston metropolitan area	2,875,000	1,052,000	1,084,000	467,000	272,000
Massachusetts (including Boston)	4,691,000	1,347,000	1,501,000	878,000	965,000

* Based on 1950 population figures.

Casualties

On the basis of the postulated attack, the specific conditions of which Ervin et al. have described in the previous article, and on the testimony of expert witnesses, the Holifield Committee compiled an estimate of the number of casualties for each area attacked. The estimates for the Boston metropolitan area and for Massachusetts as a whole, taken directly from the Committee Summary Analysis,[12] are given in Table 1. In the Boston area (hit by 10 megatons each on Boston and Cambridge and 8 megatons on Bedford), about 1,000,000 people will be killed on the first day and about 1,250,000 will be injured. Of the injured, approximately 1,000,000 die, making a total of more than 2,000,000 dead in the Boston area. Over the entire state, including the Boston area, over 1,300,000 will die immediately, over 2,300,000 will be injured, and of these about two-thirds will die.* The number of injured immediately after the attack is thus about 1,500,000 for Boston and over 2,000,000 for the entire Commonwealth.

Estimation of the number of physicians who will remain uninjured is more difficult. Data on the number of physicians within a given large target area are available.[13,14] Since the physicians of a state tend to be concentrated in the large cities and those within a metropolitan area are usually concentrated near its center, physicians face a higher risk from thermonuclear bombardment than the general population. For example, 70 per cent of the physicians of the Commonwealth live within the Boston metropolitan area[13]

* These figures differ slightly from those in the previous article because the Holifield calculations assume an unsheltered population and include the effects of radiation and blast, but attribute no casualties specifically to fire storms.

TABLE 2. *Casualties among Physicians in Metropolitan Boston and Massachusetts after a 56-Megaton Attack.*

TARGET AREA	No. OF PHYSI-CIANS IN ATTACKED AREA	No. KILLED ON 1ST DAY	No. FATALLY INJURED	No. SUR-VIVING INJURED	No. UN-INJURED
Boston metropolitan area	6,560[13]	2,380	2,470	1,070	640
Massachusetts (including Boston)	9,440[14]	2,710	3,020	1,730	1,980

whereas only 50 per cent of the total population of the Commonwealth live in this area.[15] Furthermore, some 85 per cent of the physicians of the Commonwealth live within the metropolitan areas of Boston, Worcester, Springfield-Holyoke, Fitchburg-Leominster, and Fall River,[13] each of which is scheduled for thermonuclear bombardment in the Joint Congressional Committee's estimate.[11] Although the risk for physicians is clearly higher than that for the general population, we have made the assumption that physicians are at the same risk as the population as a whole. Table 2 is based on this assumption and thus represents an *overestimate* of the number of physicians remaining uninjured. Even so, some 4800 physicians would be killed or fatally injured, 1000 would be injured, and only about 650 would remain uninjured in the Boston area. In the entire Commonwealth, including Boston, some 5700 physicians would be killed, 1700 would be injured, and only 2000 would remain uninjured. If we assume further that 25 per cent of the physicians who are nonfatally injured will be able to carry on medical duties in the postattack period despite their injuries, the number of physicians available for medical service will be about 900 in the Boston area and about 2400 in the Commonwealth as a whole.

When this calculation is examined, it is clear that it rests on still other assumptions. For example, it includes physicians of all ages, and many in at least partial retirement. This calculation also counts, as physicians available for postattack service, many whose work has centered on administration, laboratory research, or preclinical teaching rather than on clinical care of patients. Additionally, it must be remembered that this count of functioning physicians includes pathologists, psychiatrists, and other specialists who have had little recent training or experience in the treatment of burns, trauma, or radiation injury.

The data in Tables 1 and 2 yield a ratio of approximately 1700 acutely injured persons to each functioning physician in the Boston area, and about 1000 injured to 1 physician in Massachusetts as a whole. These are minimum estimates of the number of injured per physician. It must also be remembered that the total population-to-physician ratio, which includes the uninjured survivors, both healthy and ill, will be still higher.

These calculations of death and injury have been made without reference to the provision of fallout shelters. As the preceding article by Ervin and his associates and a recent editorial in the *New England Journal of Medicine*[16] clearly demonstrate, radiation shelters will be useless in the extensive area of blast and fire storm surrounding each hypo-center.

Nevertheless, it has been stated that the provision of radiation shelters will markedly reduce the number of casualties. There is little doubt that of the people fortunate enough to be outside the range of blast and fire, some who would otherwise have been irradiated would escape such injury by reaching and remaining in an adequate fallout shelter. The magnitude and relative importance of this protective effect varies, however, with the type and distribution of thermonuclear attack.[17] In the presently postulated attack on targets in Massachusetts, some 721,000 radiation deaths and 557,000 radiation injuries would be averted *if* fallout shelters were provided for the entire population, *if* the shelters were 100 per cent effective against fallout, *if* every shelter were adequately provided with food, water, an independent oxygen supply, and other necessities for inhabitation for several weeks or more, *if* warning time were adequate, and *if* transportation and the maintenance of order in a threatened population were sufficient to enable most of the population to reach shelters. Assuming that all these conditions are met, however, the presently postulated attack will still result in 1,347,000 deaths on the first day, 780,000 fatal injuries and 321,000 nonfatal injuries in Massachusetts.

The continuing radioactivity described by Ervin et al. in the preceding article will make it necessary for any survivors inside shelters to remain there for a period of weeks and then to leave only for brief periods. The same restrictions will apply to surviving physicians. Therefore, any increase in the number of uninjured physicians achieved by the provision of radiation shelters would be balanced by the fact that these physicians could not safely venture outside the shelter to aid the injured. Thus, the net effect of preserving physicians by having them remain inside radiation shelters is to reduce the number of physicians available at the time of greatest medical need—that is, for the care of the acutely injured in the immediate postattack period—though increasing the number of physicians available in subsequent weeks.

The consequences of a ratio of 1000 or 1700 acutely injured persons to 1 physician are made clear when one examines the immediate postattack situation in greater detail. If the physician were to spend an average of only fifteen minutes on diagnosis and treatment of each individual patient, and if he worked sixteen hours every day, it would require sixteen to twenty-six days before every injured person could be seen for the first time. Even this estimate, however, is unreasonably optimistic, for it assumes that every physician will be willing to expose himself to high or lethal levels of radiation and will be able to determine the areas in which he is most needed, transport himself to those areas, and find every one of the 1000 or 1700 survivors with *no* expenditure of time. If, on the other hand, the complete availability and effectiveness of fallout shelters is assumed, and all surviving physicians are sheltered, the situation changes. Under these circumstances, there will be *no* functioning physicians outside shelters in the immediate postattack period, but the injured-to-physician ratio will be considerably improved two weeks or more later, when physicians emerge from their shelters, since large numbers of the injured will have died in the interim.

The ratio of total patients to physicians in both the immediate and later postattack periods will be affected by the number of persons not physically injured in the attack who would demand the physician's time. This includes those with pre-existing illness requiring continuing medical attention and those with acute illness secondarily related or unrelated to the attack; it also includes those who merely believe they are injured. That this will be a considerable problem is indicated by past experience in much lesser catastrophes[18] in which patients not at all involved presented themselves with the appropriate symptoms. The symptoms of radiation sickness, in particular, are such that many persons exposed only minimally are likely to confront the physician with weakness, nausea, vomiting, and diarrhea. These patients, too, will require diagnosis and treatment, further reducing physician availability to the acutely injured.

It follows that most of the fatally injured persons will never see a

TABLE 3. *Massachusetts Hospitals Surviving Blast and Fire in a 56-Megaton Attack.*

TYPE	PRESENT TOTAL	OUTSIDE BLAST AREA*	OUTSIDE BLAST & FIRE-STORM AREA†
		NO. OF HOSPITALS	
General	128	68	24
Psychiatric	31	19	7
Tuberculosis	12	8	2
Chronic	9	4	2
Pediatric	3	1	0
Maternity	3	0	0
Miscellaneous	23	11	3
Totals	209	111	38
		NO. OF BEDS	
General	21,796	7,483	2,104
Psychiatric	33,937	22,963	5,899
Tuberculosis	2,139	1,712	195
Chronic	2,449	530	120
Pediatric	546	43	0
Maternity	357	0	0
Miscellaneous	4,491	3,501	1,238
Totals	65,715	36,232	9,546

* Following radiuses of blast area assumed: for 10-megaton attack, 7.0 mi.; for 8.0-megaton attack, 6.5 mi.; for 3-megaton attack, 4.7 mi.; for 2-megaton attack, 4.0 mi.; & for 1-megaton attack, 3.2 mi. These are radiuses at which blast pressure will be 5 pounds/square inch & within which brick buildings will collapse.

† Following radiuses of fire-storm area assumed: for 10-megaton attack, 23.0 mi.; for 8-megaton attack, 21.0 mi.; for 3-megaton attack, 14.0 mi.; for 2-megaton attack, 12.0 mi.; & for 1-megaton attack, 9.0 mi. These are radiuses at which thermal radiation will be 8 calories/cm.² & within which easily combustible materials will ignite.

physician, even for the simple administration of narcotics, before they die. Many of those injured who might survive with adequate care will also die, and many other injured persons will have to accomplish their survival without medical aid.

Medical Facilities

What of the injured persons who are fortunate enough to find an available physician? What facilities and equipment will remain intact for the physician to use?

A fairly accurate estimate can be made of the number of hospital beds remaining in Massachusetts after a 56-megaton attack of the distribution envisioned by the testimony before the Holifield Com-

mittee.[19] The extent of blast and fire damage is shown on the map
in the preceding article by Ervin and his associates. Table 3 summarizes the hospital destruction to be expected; this is a deliberate
underestimate since it ignores damage to Massachusetts facilities
caused by bomb explosions in Providence, Rhode Island, and Ports-
mouth, New Hampshire. Thus, even if radiation is not considered,
fewer than 10,000 of the existing 65,000 hospital beds in the Commonwealth will remain to accommodate their present occupants
in addition to 2,000,000 injured. It must be noted that over half
these remaining beds are in psychiatric hospitals. Although these
hospitals are poorly equipped to deal with traumatic injury and
radiation sickness, the beds will be needed. Psychiatric beds now
have a high occupancy rate. To make them available for victims of
thermonuclear attack it will be necessary to displace their current
occupants. If large numbers of psychiatric patients—many of them
unable to care for themselves under normal social circumstances—
are released, the consequences will be difficult to predict. It must
be noted, furthermore, that there is no medical or scientific basis
for reaching a decision about whether a patient with schizophrenia or the victim of a third-degree burn "deserves" or should be
assigned an available bed. Problems of this kind are considered
further in a later section of this article.

In an attempt to meet the problem of hospital destruction the
Federal Civil Defense Administration planned to provide 6000
200-bed improvised hospitals for the nation as a whole.[20] At the
time of writing of this article 60 of these hospitals actually have
been stored in warehouses in Massachusetts.[21] A description of
the use of 1 of these improvised hospitals has been published. [22]
If none of these were destroyed by the attack, if roads remained intact, and if manpower were available to activate all of them, they
would still provide beds for less than 1 per cent of the acutely injured in the Commonwealth.

Estimation of medical supplies remaining is extremely difficult.
At the present time most large concentrations of drugs and equipment are in the hospitals and the wholesale-drug warehouses of
the large metropolitan areas and would be destroyed. If the investment were large enough, it would be possible to cache sufficient
supplies in outlying areas to meet the needs of millions of casualties
in addition to the normal medical needs of the population. As of
1956[20] the Federal Civil Defense Administration's plan was
to disperse almost $500,000,000 worth of medical supplies in some

100 warehouses in "fringe" areas around major cities through the nation. The further cost of maintaining these supplies was not stated, but the magnitude of the problem is considerable:

> Penicillin G tablets carry a five-year dating and the parenteral preparations are not intended for use more than three or four years after formulation. Streptomycin in dry form has a four-year dating; tetracycline, two years; and erythromycin, three years. Tetanus Antitoxin has an expiration date of three years. . . .[23]

If these supply stockpiles are completed and kept up to date, if they escape blast and fire-storm damage, if transportation facilities remain intact and roads stay open, and if manpower is available to distribute them in an organized manner, they will be sufficient to treat 5,000,000 casualties in the United States for three weeks.[20] Since the Holifield estimate for the nation as a whole is 40,000,000 injured (as well as 20,000,000 killed in the first day), this large national investment will provide for less than 15 per cent of the anticipated injured. Furthermore, narcotics, one of the most essential groups of drugs in the care of seriously injured casualties, have not been stockpiled at all in Massachusetts because of difficulties in storage and handling.[21]

The absolute number of physicians, beds and supplies is only one aspect of the problem. Their distribution, in relation to the geographic distribution of the injured, is an equally critical consideration. To move physicians, ancillary personnel, and beds into attacked areas presupposes good communications and transport. Furthermore, the reluctance of physicians to leave their shelters and their own patient populations to enter areas of higher radiation danger may be supported by national policy. Any surviving physician who leaves a fallout shelter for more than a few hours in the immediate postattack period may himself suffer radiation injury.

On the other hand, the attempt of injured persons to make their way to relatively undamaged areas may precipitate grave social conflict. As Leiderman and Mendelson point out in their accompanying article, psychologic disorganization is likely under postattack conditions. In Nagasaki a surviving physician observed that ". . . those who survived the bomb were, if not merely lucky, in greater or lesser degree selfish, self-centered, guided by instinct and not civilization . . ."[24]

That similar problems to those in Nagasaki may be anticipated in the United States is demonstrated by the statements of local civil-defense officials. For example, the *Los Angeles Times* of August 5, 1961, reported a speech by the Civil Defense Coordinator of Riverside County, California, warning the citizens to arm themselves to repel the hundreds of thousands of refugees who would flee that way if Los Angeles were bombed. The *San Francisco Chronicle* of September 23, 1961, reported a speech by the Civil Defense Coordinator of Kern County, California, suggesting that people fleeing from Los Angeles be diverted into the desert by armed policemen.

The question of immediate concern to physicians, given the almost inevitable acute shortage of medical care after a 1446-megaton attack, is whether or not reactions of panic and violence will develop in the competition for access to remaining medical facilities.

The considerations reviewed thus far, serious as they are, represent only one aspect of the problems of medical planning for thermonuclear attack. Physician-to-population ratios and the survival and distribution of beds and drugs are essentially quantitative and logistic questions. But there are substantive questions as well, bearing not so much on the quantity of medical care as on its content. Given the survival of some physicians and facilities, in short, what will the doctors have to do?

New Medical Problems

In the attempt to develop methods of clinical practice and medical care in the postattack period, the experience of the armed forces in combat zones has guided planning. This involves establishment of an organization providing for an orderly process of medical management, sorting or triage of the sick and wounded according to the presenting type and urgency of the problem, deciding on priority of treatment, and evacuating those requiring extensive care to better equipped installations. The applicability of this military model, however, is limited. In a thermonuclear attack there is no clear-cut front line and safe rear area, for blast and fire effects are widespread and radiation is almost ubiquitous.

In any case, as every physician knows, clinical practice is profoundly affected by its setting. In the postattack period the physician will encounter many major disruptions of the human environment. These include destruction of transportation, communication, and electricity, contamination and depletion of food supplies, destruction of housing and fuel, destruction and pollution of public water supplies, and disruption of garbage and sewage disposal as well as other sanitary facilities.

These circumstances will, at the same time, create new medical problems and alter the management of such familiar entities as burns, fractures, and blood loss. In some ways the situation will resemble those in underdeveloped areas in which too few physicians lacking essential resources must handle large populations. The problems peculiar to nuclear attack will be superimposed.

CARE OF THE INDIVIDUAL PATIENT

The specific medical problems facing the surviving physician will include large numbers of patients with the following injuries: blast injuries, including lacerations of soft tissues and fractures; thermal injuries, including surface burns, retinal burns, and respiratory-tract damage; and radiation injuries, including acute radiation syndrome and delayed effects. Substantial numbers of patients will present infectious disease owing to lowered resistance and epidemic outbreaks[25]; others will suffer psychological breakdowns consequent to fear, grief, and trauma.[26] In addition, the physician must deal with such pre-existing medical conditions as diabetes mellitus, hypertension, and cancer.

Many medical articles have outlined optimal treatment for the types of injury most likely to be encountered after a nuclear attack: blast injuries[27-29]; thermal injuries[30-32]; radiation syndromes[33,34]; and psychiatric problems.[26] The interested physician is referred to these sources. The *feasibility* of optimal treatment for these and other conditions under postattack circumstances is germane to any analysis of nuclear-disaster planning by physicians.

The problems of trauma provide a good example. Major public concern has been with radiation injury; however, thermal and mechanical trauma will be of much greater importance. It has been estimated[32] that the radius at which the initial ionizing radiation is at the 300-rem level (sublethal) increases only by a factor of 5 from a 1-kiloton to a 20-megaton air burst. The same increase from 1 kiloton to 20 megatons increases by a factor of 27 the radius of blast-induced pressures of 2.5 pounds per square inch. Thermal energy sufficient to cause second-degree burns increases by a factor of 64, from a radius of 0.5 mile to a radius of 32 miles. It has been concluded, on this basis, that burn injury is likely to cause the greatest number of casualties in any nuclear explosion.

Optimal therapy for serious burns requires sedation, oxygen administration, and large intravenous infusions of fluids. Antibiotics, tetanus prophylaxis, and local wound care will also be necessary. Even if the individual physician is well instructed in the modern care of serious burns, it is difficult to see how he will cope with hundreds of such patients at once when he is lacking the most essential diagnostic and therapeutic facilities.

In the patients with thermal injuries, diagnosis and triage may be difficult and preclude prompt judgment and decision. But thousands of patients will also present fractures, ruptures of internal organs, penetrating wounds of the skull or thorax, and infections; many, in fact, will suffer all these and burns as well. How are these problems to be identified and treated rationally in the absence of adequate x-ray and other diagnostic facilities? The question is important since decisions will have to be made to abandon the care of many. Patients with fatal or nearly fatal injuries may be neglected to make care available to more salvageable ones, and primary attention may be assigned to those who have the greatest possibility of survival. Triage for this or any other purpose is made even more difficult by the presence of radiation injury. The early clinical pictures of psychogenic nausea and diarrhea and of moderate, sublethal and lethal radiation injury overlap, and the medical history will be of little use since few patients will be able to report their exposure accurately. The necessity of making quick judgments involving life-and-death decisions for individual patients after only cursory examination, and the possible decision to ignore the critically ill and the near dying, would represent a profound and difficult reversal in the attitudes and performance of the physician.

In the face of these difficulties, many civil-defense plans place considerable reliance on nurses and on the training of large numbers of laymen in self-care and first aid. Once again, this attempt is drawn from military models and requires critical examination for the postulated postattack situation. There is no doubt that many minor injuries can be treated satisfactorily by first-aid measures and that some more seriously injured persons—for example, those with active hemorrhage—will be saved. Complicated problems involving a mixture of thermal, blast, and other traumatic injuries will be beyond the competence of most nurses and laymen, however, and unfortunately will be of frequent occurrence. Careful consideration makes it clear that first aid is essentially a "holding" operation, effective only on the assumption that adequate medical care will be provided later. Yet the simple logistics of physicians, beds, and supplies make it extremely unlikely that any subsequent and more skilled medical care will be available within a reasonable time.

PUBLIC-HEALTH PROBLEMS

The medical problems of the postattack period will require more of a public-health orientation than many practicing physicians have hitherto utilized.[25,35] In a society struggling for survival adequate sanitation and the provision of food and water may save more lives than the most skilled specialist care. For example, Beckjord discusses the problem of water supply[25]:

The military and civilians are accustomed to having anywhere from 50 to 150 gal. of water per person per day for all purposes, including bathing. After an enemy attack on our large cities, the individual will be very fortunate to have even a quart of water per day. The importance of having an adequate water supply, regardless of its potability, has not been sufficiently stressed if we are to keep people alive and to suppress dysentery through personal hygiene.

The control of epidemic disease will constitute an ever present challenge. As Ervin et al. have shown in the preceding paper, it is likely that the vectors of epidemic disease would survive radiation injury better than the human population. Eastern equine encephalitis, hepatitis, poliomyelitis, and other endemic disease could easily reach epidemic proportions under these circumstances. The radiation might also cause new mutant forms of bacteria and viruses, some of which could be highly infective in the absense of immune defenses. Furthermore, the lessening of host resistance by radiation exposure, malnutrition, excessive fatigue, and severe emotional stress would render human beings susceptible to bacteria or fungi that are not normally invasive. Poor hygienic conditions and inadequate medical facilities would contribute to the epidemic potential.[36]

Among the new public-health problems will be disposal of the dead. Although this problem has not received extensive discussion in most articles dealing with the medical consequences of thermonuclear attack, the fact that there will be almost 3,000,000 bodies in Massachusetts alone suggests that a serious hazard to the health of the remaining public will exist. Documented experience with certain past disasters provides some comparative data; this will be examined in greater detail as an example of the gap between current planning and the actual problems to be faced.

As the Joint Congressional Committee on Atomic Energy has estimated, there will be approximately 2,800,000 dead in Massachusetts, including 2,100,000 in the Boston metropolitan area alone. These deaths will occur in two peaks; a calculation of the United States Army Mortuary Service suggests that, "due to the latent period of radio-injury, an upward curve in the death rate should be evident at two weeks postattack, reach a maximum at four to six weeks and gradually subside during the following six months." [37]

Prompt disposal of corpses will be essential for many reasons. Some of the public-health problems are obvious—for example, the need for control of epidemic disease and its vectors, flies and rodents. An equally important, though less apparent, reason is psychological. There is evidence[38] that profound emotional disorders and somatic manifestations follow the sight and smell of decomposing bodies.

Explicit consideration has been given to this problem by health officers of the Office of Civil and Defense Mobilization, and it is instructive to review their comments.[37] In an attack in which the maximum weapon size is 20 megatons, they make the following observation:

> . . . it is logical to assume that most combustibles as well as the dead on the surface within a 10 to 11 mile radius of such a weapon burst will either be vaporized or incinerated through the resultant firestorm . . . intense radiation [will prevent] little more than heroic rescue in the 10 to 20 mile zone for several weeks. What cadavers might be recovered are those on the fringe of the blast area and upwind . . . The city is lost and rehabilitation is unthinkable until residual radio-activity has effaced itself. It may be far simpler to build new cities elsewhere and allow the dead to sleep in their memorial.

The Boston area may thus become a mausoleum. The same authors note that "for obvious public health reasons, the demolished city must be fenced in or cordoned and placed under quarantine . . . there is little need to consider large-scale removal and disposal of the dead for the blast area."

In fringe areas, however, the problems and plans differ. Here, the same source suggests, "regular procedures of the peacetime mortuary service can be preserved, including collection, identification, record-keeping, religious rites, and burial. Little need be changed from normal routine except adjustment to greater quantities of dead."

When the assumptions implied in this account are examined, however, it is difficult to accept it as a realistic prospect for Massachusetts. The description of highly efficient, mobile, smoothly operating burial services assumes the maintenance of transportation, the survival of adequate medical facilities at which the dying might congregate, and the existence of a high degree of motivation and social organization. Residual levels of radioactivity will sharply limit the safe working time of mortuary teams. Finally, it must be noted that bodies exposed to the atmosphere will be covered with radioactive particles; disposal thus becomes a problem akin to the disposal of radioactive waste, which, even in peacetime, has required extensive technical equipment and special skills.

Data from official military sources on an earlier attempt to dispose of the bodies of wartime casualties may illuminate the magnitude of the postnuclear task. When the United States Army entered Manila in 1944, it faced the problem of burying 39,000 bodies of Japanese and Filipinos killed during the preceding week.[39] It was soon found that American troops were unable to withstand the psychological aspects of this work, and "with a few exceptions, nausea, vomiting, and loss of appetite occurred after a few days." Local laborers were recruited at double pay to place the dead in large pits; nevertheless, the burial of these 39,000 dead, unhampered by such complications as radioactivity, required eight weeks.

It is difficult to comprehend such consequences of the postulated attack as the existence of more than 2,000,000 dead, and it is distasteful to dwell at length on the technics of disposal. However, the difficulties exemplify the unprecedented problems physicians and the public may face, and emphasize the fact that planning based primarily on previous disasters is inadequate to deal with the scope and magnitude of a thermonuclear attack.

Ethical Problems for the Physician

The postattack medical responsibilities that we have described will challenge the physician with alternatives that have profound ethical implications. There has been little discussion, however, of the specific ethical problems likely to occur.

For example, what is the physician's relative responsibility to himself, to his family, to his preattack patients, to acutely injured casualties and to any society that may remain? The individual questions that these conflicting demands raise are numerous. Does the physician remain at his post and neglect his family? Dr. Takashi Nagai,[40] a physician of Nagasaki, states in an autobiography:

> I was an officer of the College First Aid and Rescue Committee, and I was so conscious of my position, so concerned about doing what I felt was expected of me as an officer of the Rescue Committee, that it was over two full days before I got to my home where my wife lay dead. I discharged my responsibility. What will be my reward in the eyes of [my children] when they are grown?

Does the physician seek shelter? The following recent examples illustrate the intensity of feeling on this issue. Dr. J. C. Cain,[41] of the Mayo Clinic, states: "We must first protect ourselves . . . Remember that a sick or dead doctor is of no value to his country. . . ." An article by Dr. G. C. Chalmers[42] (a pseudonym) in *Medical Economics* asserts:

> If my community is hit, my obligation as a doctor will be greater than ever. And if I'm to go on functioning as I should, not only must *I survive,* but my family as well. So I've built a blast shelter beneath my front yard . . . There are two precautions I've taken in case a nuclear catastrophe interrupts the normal enforcement of law and order. I've taught my family a special knock code as a signal for opening the shelter's thick, steel-plated door. And I've stocked the shelter with firearms and ammunition.

Dr. Eugene V. Parsonnett,[43] in a commentary on this article, strongly disagrees:

> I suppose Dr. Chalmers plans to remain in his secure little shelter, having morally protected himself and his immediate family, having probably had to shoot to death some stray friends and acquaintances who may have wished to invade his sanctuary . . . I find it inconceivable that people who proudly bear the name of doctor can isolate themselves from family, friends, and society in this immoral kind of seclusion.

If the physician finds himself in an area high in radiation, does he leave the injured to secure his own safety? Is the neglect of his patients under these circumstances justifiable because many patients will profit from his help in other areas?

Other ethical problems are raised by the necessity for allocation of the inadequate supply of physicians and resources. When faced with hundreds of severely injured patients, how does the physician select those to be treated first? How does he choose between saving the lives of the few and easing the pain of the many? How does he allocate limited supplies of narcotics and analgesics?

In Hiroshima and Nagasaki, a number of embryos exposed to radiation *in utero* were born with malformations.[44] If there is a place for therapeutic abortion after rubella in the first trimester, as seems widely accepted,[45] is there a place for mass abortion in the postattack period?

Finally, when analgesics are limited or unavailable, what is the physician's responsibility to the fatally injured or those with incurable disease? Which of his duties—the prolongation of life or the relief of pain—takes precedence? Regardless of his own professional training and convictions, the physician will daily face demands from patients for euthanasia on a scale and with an intensity unparalleled in his past experience.

Neither the Hippocratic Oath, the published codes of ethics of the American Medical Association, nor the personal morality on which every physician relies provides an easy answer to these questions. In fact, a review of these trusted and cherished guides in the light of the problems of thermonuclear war makes them seem curiously and sadly obsolete, as if they reflected the human innocence of an earlier era.

Discussion

The thermonuclear attack on the United States postulated by the Holifield Committee has been shown to lead to medical problems quantitatively greater and qualitatively different from any ever faced before. Although it might be feasible through sufficient economic investment and at the cost of public and physician regimentation to prepare a disaster plan to meet this postulated attack, such a plan would neither prevent the loss of millions of lives nor be effective against other types of attack. A change in any of the relevant variables such as the addition of a second strike or more bombs in a different distribution could nullify defenses prepared against the type of attack postulated by the Holifield Committee.

There is, to our knowledge, no scientific basis for accurate prediction of the pattern of an enemy attack—except, perhaps, to note that the most unlikely pattern is the one against which an enemy knows that elaborate disaster plans have been prepared.

It is deeply misleading, therefore, to speak of any single disaster plan as a secure answer to the hazards of thermonuclear war. It is deeply misleading to focus on radiation shelters while ignoring the problems of blast and fire storm. And it is deeply misleading to propose patterns of medical treatment without examining the magnitude of the task or the availability of resources in sufficient detail to reveal the nature of the anticipated problems.

To select a disaster plan is to make an uncertain prediction—in plainer words, to gamble on the nature of the attack. Physicians interested in rational consideration of any given medical plan for nuclear attack must recognize the nature of the vast gamble with human lives that selection of this plan would represent. Since it is impossible to prepare adequately for every possible type of nuclear attack, the physician's responsibility goes beyond mere disaster planning. Physicians, charged with the responsibility for the lives of their patients and the health of their communities, must also explore a new area of preventive medicine, the prevention of thermonuclear war.

Summary

The medical consequences in Massachusetts of a 1446-megaton thermonuclear attack on the United States are analyzed. Of 6560 physicians in the Boston metropolitan area, approximately 900 functioning physicians would remain; of the 9440 in the Commonwealth as a whole, 2400 would still be available. The resultant injured-to-physician ratio would be over 1000 to 1; the total patient-to-physician ratio would be much greater. Of 65,000 hospital beds in the Commonwealth, 10,000 would remain to serve their present occupants in addition to 2,000,000 injured. Medical supplies would be inadequate. Competition by survivors for the remaining facilities and supplies would be likely to raise new problems.

These quantitative increases in medical needs would lead inexorably to qualitative changes in the type of medicine practiced. Some of the problems to be expected in the care of the individual patient, in public-health measures, and in decisions of an ethical nature are examined in detail. The implications for disaster planning are discussed.

References

1. *After the A Bomb: Emergency care in atomic warfare.* Edited by C. F. Behrens. 182 pp. New York: Nelson, 1951.
2. Sears, T. P. *The Physician in Atomic Defense: Atomic principles, biologic reaction and organization for medical defense.* 308 pp. Chicago: Yearbook Publishers, 1953.
3. Mass casualties: principles involved in management: symposium. *Mil. Med. 118*:247-435, April, 1956.
4. Council on National Defense. *J.A.M.A. 171*:189-225, 1959.
5. Medical planning for disaster: symposium. *California Med. 93*:69-98, 1960.
6. Disaster medical care: symposium. *California Med. 95*:353-366, 1961.
7. Garb, S. Survival in thermonuclear war. I, II, III, IV, V, VI, VII, VIII, IX, X. *New York State J. Med. 60*:2440-4064, 1960. Survival in thermonuclear war. *Ibid. 61*:136-300, 1961.
8. King, R. E. Survival in nuclear warfare. *Ciba Clin. Symposia 14* (1): 1-33, 1962.
9. *Medical Effects of the Atomic Bomb in Japan.* Edited by A. W. Oughterson and S. Warren. 477 pp. New York: McGraw-Hill, 1956. (*National Nuclear Energy Series,* Manhattan Project Technical Section, Division VIII—Vol. 8.)
10. Lichter, N. Medical news: physicians must take lead in civil defense. *J.A.M.A. 178*: Adv. p. 36 (December 2), 1961.
11. United States Congress, Joint Committee on Atomic Energy. *Biological and Environmental Effects of Nuclear War: Summary analysis of hearings, June 22-26, 1959.* 58 pp. Washington, D. C.: Government Printing Office, 1959.
12. Ibid.[11] Pp. 19 and 20.
13. American Medical Association. *American Medical Directory, 1960-61: A register of physicians of the U. S., Isthmian Canal Zone, Puerto Rico, Virgin Islands and certain U. S. protectorates: Who possess a degree of doctor of medicine or its equivalent from an approved medical school or from a bona fide medical school.* Twenty-first edition. 1693 pp. Chicago: The Association, 1961. Pp. 493-533.
14. United States Department of Health, Education, and Welfare, Division of Public Health Methods. Stewart, W. H., and Pennell, M. Y. *Physicians' Age, Type of Practice and Location.* 199 pp. Washington, D. C.: Government Printing Office, 1960. (*Health Manpower Source Book, 10.*)
15. United States Bureau of Budgets, Office of Statistical Standards. *Standard Metropolitan Statistical Areas.* 48 pp. Washington, D. C.: Government Printing Office, 1961.
16. Editorial. Realities of civil defense. *New Eng. J. Med. 266*:520, 1962.
17. United States Congress, Joint Committee on Atomic Energy.[11] P. 17.

18. Powell, J. W., Raynor, J., and Finesinger, J. E. Responses to disaster in American cultural groups. In National Research Council and Army Medical Service Graduate School. *Symposium on Stress: Sponsored jointly by the Division of Medical Sciences, National Research Council and Army Medical Service Graduate School, Walter Reed Medical Center.* 332 pp. Washington, D. C.: Government Printing Office, 1953. Pp. 174-193.

19. Listing of Hospitals. *J. Am. Hosp. A.* (Guide Issue) *33*:96-102, 1959.

20. Whitney, J. M. Federal Civil Defense Administration medical stockpile. *Mil. Med. 118*:260, 1956.

21. Hogan, C. L. Chief of Medical Service, Massachusetts Civil Defense Agency. Personal communication.

22. Hampton, J. K., Jr. Operation AFTA. *J.A.M.A. 169*:378-380, 1959.

23. Rice, R. M. Medicinal supplies for mass casualties from pharmaceutical producer's viewpoint. *Mil. Med. 118*:262, 1956.

24. Nagai, T. *We of Nagasaki: The story of survivors in an atomic wasteland.* Translated by I. Shirato and H. B. L. Silverman. 189 pp. New York: Duell, 1951. Pp. 179 and 180.

25. Beckjord, P. R. Public health aspects of preventive medicine and disaster. *J.A.M.A. 171*:212-217, 1959.

26. Glass, A. J. Management of mass psychiatric casualties. *Mil. Med. 118*:335-342, 1956.

27. O'Donoghue, J. A. Mechanical and secondary missile injuries. *Mil. Med. 118*:271-273, 1956.

28. Shaeffer, J. R. Treatment of mass mechanical injuries. *Mil. Med. 118*: 314-318, 1956.

29. Moncrief, W. H., Jr. Management of soft-tissue trauma after nuclear strike. *J.A.M.A. 171*:209-212, 1959.

30. Pearse, H. E. Thermal injuries of nuclear warfare. *Mil. Med. 118*: 274-278, 1956.

31. Miller, D. W. Mass thermal burns. *Mil. Med. 118*:319-325, 1956.

32. Vogel, E. H., Jr. Management of burns resulting from nuclear disaster. *J.A.M.A. 171*:205-208, 1959.

33. Lyon, G. M. Radiation injuries resulting from nuclear explosion and fallout. *Mil. Med. 118*:279-285, 1956.

34. Cronkite, E. P. Treatment of radiation injuries. *Mil. Med. 118*:328-334, 1956.

35. Stevenson, A. H., and Smith, R. L. Public health and sanitation problems in nuclear warfare. *Mil Med. 118*:381-385, 1956.

36. Lesser, G. T. Unpublished data.

37. Moore, G., and Lindquist, P. A. Civilian mortuary service and thermonuclear war. *Mil. Med. 125*:467-474, 1960.

38. Nagai, T.[24] Pp. 123 and 124.

39. Orth, G. L. Disaster and disposal of dead. *Mil. Med. 124*:505-510, 1959.

40. Nagai, T.[24] P. 181.

41. Cain, J. C. Quoted in Medical News: Mayo Clinic prepares for nuclear war. *J.A.M.A. 179*: Adv. p. 42 (January 27), 1962.

42. Chalmers, G. C. Should doctors go underground? *M. Econ. 39* (6): 99-104 (March 12), 1962.

43. Parsonnett, E. V. Immoral kind of seclusion? *M. Econ. 39* (6):102 (March 12), 1962.
44. Hollingsworth, J. W. Delayed radiation effects in survivors of atomic bombings: summary of findings of Atomic Bomb Casualty Commission, 1947-1959. *New Eng. J. Med. 263*:481-487, 1960.
45. Reid, D. E. *Textbook of Obstetrics.* 1087 pp. Philadelphia: Saunders, 1962. P. 253.

Some Psychiatric Considerations in Planning for Defense Shelters

P. HERBERT LEIDERMAN, M.D., and
JACK H. MENDELSON, M.D.

DURING RECENT YEARS much attention has been given to the physical and biological problems of defending oneself against the perils of the nuclear age.[1,2,3] There has been relatively less publicly acknowledged concern with the psychological and social implications of the proposals dealing with the problem of nuclear war, though two recent publications[4,5] are an indication that this may well be the major focus of activity for the immediate future. Rather than attempt to deal with all of the myriad psychiatric problems associated with the nuclear age, we shall purposely limit ourselves to a consideration of the shelter program, since many of the psychological and social issues of the nuclear age are brought into focus by even the mere suggestion of such a program. Broad, and perhaps more important, social and psychological considerations involved in the stress of living and survival in the nuclear age will be discussed in other papers, and has been the focus of a symposium held at the American Association for the Advancement of Science.[6] This paper, therefore, will be addressed to two major issues: 1) The psychological impact on the individual and community in planning for a defense shelter program; 2) the psychological and social problems related to shelter utilization in the event of a nuclear holocaust.

Planning for a Shelter Program

Although man has had experience with limited disasters such as war, tornados, earthquakes, floods, and epidemics, he has never been confronted with *planning* for a potential disaster on a global scale. Expert and near-expert persons have suggested, however, that the current situation is similar to events experienced in the past, at least in regard to threat of war. To the extent that this point of view is applicable, we shall use data from studies of relatively limited disasters to help us understand present reactions and perhaps predict future behavior. In particular we should like to emphasize the nature of the differences between acute, relatively short-term stress and chronic, prolonged stress. The nature of the cold war and even the hot war, for the survivors, demands that we take cognizance of the *chronic* as well as of the *acute* psychological issues. Famine, slavery, and plague might be more relevant historical social experiences to draw on than military conflicts of relatively limited duration.[7,8]

Another aspect of the current situation, differentiating it from the past, is the marked urbanization of our society. There is a greater degree of interdependence than ever before. The social fabric has become more tightly woven and one might question whether it can sustain tears as in the past. A consequence of this increased interdependence is that the needs and expectancies of man have become progressively dependent upon organized social activities. The era of the isolated frontiersman caring for himself in a hostile environment has been relegated to other continents. Thus, it is not surprising that the introduction of an *individual* shelter building program evoked many hostile responses, ranging from "We won't build one" to "We'll build it and arm it." Other individuals expressed fear, apathy, and confusion when faced with a novel, ambiguous situation in which they alone were asked to be responsible for themselves. The data on the individual and group responses which we shall present should be considered against the background of an organized society with many problems of a long-term nature awaiting solution.

The assessment of public response to the shelter building program may provide a clue to the expected behavior of individuals who might want to build and use a shelter. Since this assessment is not yet complete, it might be well to examine the views of two distinguished commentators on public affairs, Hanson Baldwin, military analyst of the *New York Times*, and Arthur Krock, political writer, of the same paper. Hanson Baldwin writes:[9]

At the same time, a national shelter program could have two other seemingly disparate but concurrent effects of considerable political, psychological, and military importance.

It could induce a mistaken sense of security in the American people, a Maginot Line psychology. It would at the same time emphasize in the American mind even more than in the past the dangers of radioactivity with a consequent hobbling and hampering effect upon any resumption of atmospheric nuclear testing by the United States and on our diplomacy in general.

In psychological terms this mistaken sense of security at the *extreme* can lead either to undue apathy, or to unwarranted impulsive behavior. A situation could develop that, at a time when appropriate and legitimate demands are made upon the individual to respond to danger, he may not be prepared to respond appropriately. The boy crying "Wolf" is a well-known tale.

Arthur Krock raises another issue. In discussing the Office of Civil and Defense Mobilization pamphlet,[10] he states:[11]

The appeal of the pamphlet, despite the President's shift from his original encouragement of private shelter-building to constructions for community protection, nevertheless is principally a guide for the more fortunate—"fortunate" in having the money to build the private shelters so elaborately described, or in being sufficiently remote from a blast area to survive. But, hopefully, there seem to be numerous Americans who reject as immoral and degrading the booklet blueprints—for $150 and up—of the cellars and the backyards their superior resources permit. And hopefully, too, there seem to be numerous Americans who get the opposite of comfort from the thought of survival because of a chance location.

The divisive aspects of the program, raising such issues as urban vs. rural, rich vs. poor, West vs. East, North vs. South, will undoubtedly demand major consideration. The emphasis on the selection of individuals and groups to be saved is particularly troublesome, whether the choice is made by self-selection or government fiat. Margaret Mead,[12] at a recent AAAS Symposium in Denver, 1961, suggested that an international program be developed where certain recently married couples be provided their honeymoon underground in a blastproof shelter. By this scheme she argues that, at any given point in time, a reasonable number of the breeding population would be protected from annihilation in event of an attack. The serious introduction of such a possibility by an eminent anthropologist points up the magnitude of some of the issues in even planning a defense shelter program. That a shelter program might include only individuals of a specified age or with specified talents, but not all of them, emphasizes, at the very least, the importance of discussing the moral and ethical considerations included in a shelter program.

Perhaps the most important consideration in the discussion of planning for survival in the nuclear age is the effect upon our children. While there have been few formal studies on their reactions, Escalona points up some of the issues in a popular pamphlet.[13] The immature organism is particularly sensitive to physical and psychological trauma and it would be anticipated that many of the doubts and confusions of our age would be reflected in children in an exaggerated form. Anxiety, apathy, and indifference have been particularly evident. The psychological legacy of the threat of nuclear war will continue to live on in a future generation long after the danger has passed. Thus, the long-term psychological as well as the biogenetic by-product of nuclear threats must be considered in the planning of the type of program outlined by the Department of Defense. That such consideration has not been given is obvious from the lack of public discussion on this question.

Problems Related to Shelter Utilization

The two atomic bombs dropped on Hiroshima and Nagasaki represent the only actual experience that man has had with nuclear war. Since these cases are the only ones available, they deserve close clinical scrutiny. These attacks were followed by massive psychological and social consequences. Hachiya,[14] a Japanese physician at Hiroshima, writes of events after the blast:

Parents, half crazy with grief, searched for their children. Husbands looked for their wives, and children for their parents. One poor woman, insane with anxiety, walked aimlessly here and there through the hospital calling her child's name.

. . . What a weak fragile thing man is before the forces of destruction. After the flash the entire population had been reduced to a common level of physical and mental weakness. Those who were able walked silently towards the suburbs and distant hills, their spirits broken, their initiative gone. When asked whence they had come, they pointed to the city and said "that way"; and when asked where they were going, pointed away from the city and said "this way." They were so broken and confused that they moved and behaved like automatons.

Their reactions had astonished outsiders who reported with amazement the spectacle of long files of people holding stolidly to a narrow rough path, where close by was a smooth easy road going in the same direction. The outsiders could not grasp the fact that they were witnessing the exodus of a people who walked in the realm of dreams.

About Nagasaki, Nagai[15] writes:

From that time . . . everybody seemed to be going crazy.

In general then, those who survived . . . were the people who ignored their friends crying out in extremis . . . selfish, self-centered, guided by instinct and not civilization . . . and we know it, we who have survived.

Neither of the populations involved anticipated, nor were in any way prepared for, the havoc produced by nuclear weapons, although there were some preparations for and experience with conventional bombing. It is not only the accounts of stress and physical suffering resulting from these nuclear attacks that have impressed students of behavioral science, but the enormous impact of these events upon an entire nation, the majority of whose citizens were not directly exposed to the physical hazards of the attack itself.[16,17]

What other sources of data are available by which to assess the psychological and social response patterns of American communities following a nuclear attack? Though the data are not directly related to wartime conditions, we shall attempt to draw on the material available, recognizing the limitations involved.

Assuming that a period of warning would exist before a nuclear attack, what behavior might be anticipated during this period of threat of impending disaster? Ideally, where shelters existed, one would hope there would be an orderly procession to places of maximum security even though the interval before the attack was relatively short. The following account, quoted from a symposium on stress,[18] reveals the degree of variation of response during a fifteen-minute interval of warning before the destruction of a small town by a tornado.

Behavior during the 10 to 15 minutes under the threat varied in interesting ways. From the sample of our interviews one would judge that most of the men went home for their wives, and most of the women tended to go home to their mothers . . . The duration of the warning and threat periods determines in part how much survival action is possible. Many survivors in discussing these periods felt guilty that they had not done more or assumed more responsibility when something could have been done to help. Two people who showed depressive reactions during the remedial phases revealed that they had acted helplessly during the threat and impact phases. This behavior had mobilized guilt feelings—and also defenses against guilt.

An excellent appraisal of some of the factors involved in both individual and group response to disaster is given in a summary by Demerath[19] of a symposium on adaptation to disaster. On the basis of study of a variety of disasters he concluded that the individual responses depend upon the destructive forces involved, particularly as they impinge on the social situation and cohesiveness of the society, the initial perception and behavior of the persons affected, the organizational structure and situations in the postdisaster phase.

Of particular interest, Demerath points out that social disorganization is greater as the disastrous force is more rapid, the period of forewarning briefer, the disaster agent less well known and less clearly perceived, the physical destructiveness greater and the length of time in which the force acts is greater. These are the probable conditions of nuclear attack.

In the design and construction of shelters primary attention has been given to radiation hazards. The problem of family and community shelters against blast and thermal effects of megaton bombs has yet to be worked out. Radiation hazards are unique when compared with the dangers sustained by civilian populations during World War II air raids. The dangers encountered during conventional bombings were, for the most part, associated with information that anyone could obtain through his sensory modalities during the actual period of impact. The usual air-raid warning systems informed the public when the attack was imminent and, in addition, announced when the threat of danger had passed. Even if no air-raid warning device was available, a person could judge the magnitude of danger via his auditory, visual and tactile modalities. One can neither hear, feel, touch, smell nor see radiation. Radiation-detection equipment, of course, would provide some information to help a person make reliable judgments of the degree and duration of fallout dangers, if he had the technical skills to use the equipment.

It has been shown in previous studies of disaster that threats or dangers that cannot be perceived by the senses can have tremendous psychological impact. An example of such a situation was the mass poisoning by bootleg whisky (containing methyl alcohol) resulting in the death or blindness of nearly 50 people in Atlanta, Georgia.[20] A large number of persons drank the contaminated whisky, but were, of course, unable to detect the presence of toxic substances by taste, color or odor; furthermore, there was a period of latency between ingestion and the appearance of toxic effects. As the number of deaths and the incidence of blindness increased in the community, mounting publicity and official warnings were issued to the population. A report on the consequent behavior states:

> From the 433 clinic sheets examined, of every ten who were treated in the Emergency Clinic of Grady Hospital, four were negative to the test which the hospital was using. Two frankly said, "Doctor, I do not know whether I had it or not. Please check me over." And only four apparently justified treatment in the eyes of the medical staff.

It seems reasonable to conclude that many individuals in a population exposed to a danger undetectable by sight, sound, touch or taste will respond with symptoms even though they are not actually injured, or even exposed to danger. Even if shelters do, in fact, provide protection against fallout, many individuals may emerge with "symptoms" that may hamper or cripple their effectiveness.

Another type of situation that may be employed to help predict the behavior of individuals and groups subjected to prolonged involuntary isolation in a physically hostile environment is that of nuclear-powered submarines. The crews of these submarines are confined for long periods in restricted quarters and are in danger of potential exposure to a radiation hazard during the course of their cruise. Psychological studies have been made on the responses of such crews.[21] Although these studies are not generally available, published statements emphasize the fact that major efforts have been made to provide the crews of nuclear vessels with a maximum degree of comfort and security.

The problems of isolation for long periods, a condition that would exist in a fallout-shelter environment, may be better understood from studies concerned with the effects of sensory deprivation, isolation and confinement on man.[22] Anecdotal reports by explorers and shipwrecked sailors suggest that a variety of aberrant behavior may be evoked by sustained isolation in an environment that is potentially physically hazardous.[23] The reports of Admiral Byrd[24] during his isolation in a shelter designed to protect him against the forces of the Antarctic climate attest to the fact that prolonged isolation may lead to symptoms of oppression and depression, as well as difficulties in cognition and perception. Studies from hospitals[25] have shown that isolation superimposed on illness, even though physical care is adequate, can result in severe abnormalities of behavior. Experimental studies[26] have shown that both short-term and long-term isolation and confinement can have a variety of behavioral consequences ranging from anxiety and the appearance of somatic complaints to symptoms of hallucinations and delusional thinking. It should be pointed out that the isolation imposed in experimental studies is a relatively mild stress because the subject may escape from his isolated environment at any time by merely requesting release. This possibility of escape from a bomb shelter would not exist, and the degree of psychological decompensation can be expected to be more pronounced than in experimental studies. On the other hand, in the actual life situation, appropriate adaptive responses ensuring survival would also be called forth. Thus, the assessment of any individual response is extremely difficult to predict purely from laboratory study.

If the shelter-building program is predicated on individual family shelters, information on the confinement of small family groups becomes relevant. It should be obvious that only under the most fortuitous circumstances would an entire urban family be expected to be in the shelter together during and after an attack. Families in small towns and rural areas might be expected to be together. Systematic studies of families forced to live under conditions of isolation have been few in number and generally without pretense of scientific rigor. Vernon[27] studied one family, consisting of parents and 3 children, 2 of preschool and 1 of grammar-school age. They remained in a shelter for two weeks. The psychological effects, he reports, were minimal, though there were behavioral problems related to the high heat and humidity within the shelter. It seems apparent that for self-selected volunteers, under conditions where they know relief from confinement is possible at any time, and no disaster has occurred, short-term stays of up to fourteen days are feasible. Other anecdotal reports of families living in shelters have been less optimistic. Obviously, there are wide differences in behavior, depending on the type of family constellation and adaptability to stress. Enforced social contact will tend to heighten whatever adaptive and maladaptive mechanisms are usually employed. Perhaps one of the most beneficial by-products of the defense-shelter problem could be more imaginative, intensive studies of family interaction under conditions of isolation.

Other sources of information on the response of urban family groups to enforced isolation are the reports of Jews in hiding in Nazi Europe. The documentation regarding the plight of these Jews, some of whom remained in hiding for years, is usually in the form of diaries, or reconstruction of events after rescue. The prototype of many such accounts is the *Diary of Anne Frank*,[28] which reveals some of the potential for adaptive and maladaptive behavior in the setting of family and relatively close friends. Another book deals with the problem of the few survivors of the Warsaw ghetto,[29] where individuals of separated families, including children and elderly people, remained underground for several months. This book is revealing for the generation of despair, depression, homicide, and suicide attendant upon massive threat. However, in these groups the danger was one that was available to the senses, devastating but corporeal. The problem, related to unseen, unfelt radiation, would undoubtedly be somewhat different.

Although there have been several well-documented studies concerned with the effects of isolation on the individual in confined circumstances, there have been only a few laboratory studies concerned with group behavior under conditions of confinement. One study, designed specifically to test the effects of shelter living on a self-selected group of men, women and children, members of several families ranging in age from seven to seventy-two years, was conducted by the American Institute for Research.[30] The study consisted of 4 groups of 30 individuals each. Three groups remained in a simulated shelter for one week, and 1 group remained for two weeks. The major experimental variables were temperature and the presence or absence of a designated and trained shelter manager.

The chief findings were that the presence of a manager increased overall adjustment to shelter living and that there was reasonable tolerance of shelter temperatures up to 85°F. The absence of adequate leadership led to a breakdown in established standards of conduct, with such behavior as teen-age petting, gambling, and use of vulgar language, all of which were particularly disturbing to the older members of the group. According to the findings, adequate leadership was able to cope with such problems as sleeping difficulties, sexual tensions, hostility to other shelter occupants, claustrophobic reactions and depression. It is not unexpected that such psychological reactions should occur; however, it would have been desirable for the authors to have cited in greater detail the frequency and severity of such reactions.

The maximum tolerated temperature appeared to be 85°F. Regarding the type of discomfort reported, humidity combined with temperature rated second, being exceeded only by complaints of lack of water. Other elements that made for discomfort, in order of frequency of mention, were lack of exercise, crowding, dirt, sleeping difficulties, noise, physical symptoms, food, and the behavior of others. Agitation and tension were greatest immediately after shelter entry and before release. The desire to leave mounted steadily throughout the confinement period. Only 1 subject, a self-designated leader of a group, had to be removed from the shelter on the sixth day at the request of several mothers who "feared for the safety of their children." It is evident from the description of his behavior that he suffered a paranoid reaction. He appeared to recover his preshelter level of adjustment within hours after being removed from the shelter. The remainder of the group completed the experimental confinement period.

The authors of this study conclude that the major problem areas in an adequate shelter program are competent management, provision for sleep and minimization of conflict of social, moral, and ethical values. They recognize the following limitations in presenting their findings: all the subjects in the study were sympathetic to the shelter program; it was a *simulated* shelter situation; and the termination date of the stay was known to all members of the group before shelter entry.

Other studies of groups, conducted by the West German Government,[31] the Swedish Government[32] and the United States Navy[33] on group living have less relevance because either military men or prison volunteers were used as subjects. One finding that is important for this discussion was as follows:

During the first 3 days, about three-fourths of the testees stated that they felt well-balanced or cheerful; during the remaining 2 days, only half of them made that statement. The remaining testees stated that they were quite depressed or restless, cross or edgy. Two of them complained of agoraphobia and felt that the constant co-existence amid the group was unbearable.[31]

The performance of meaningful tasks appeared to alleviate some of the feelings of anxiety evidenced in this study, a finding corroborated by polar studies.[34]

The major finding in this survey of studies in the problems of shelter habitation is the remarkable lack of well-controlled research on meaningful areas. Physicians recognize that before any therapeutic program is instituted, a series of investigative procedures that utilize the best available scientific methods are necessary. These studies have not yet been made. It should be clear that a national endeavor of the type represented by the shelter program will bring about profound changes in the American social scene. For example, prolonged confinement, or the mere anticipation of it, is a condition so different from previous experience of most people that one could not reasonably predict the reactions of individuals to such a circumstance without further study. It would seem essential that a program of psychological and sociological research be instituted before a $20-billion shelter program is embarked upon.

Discussion

Although we have outlined some of the psychological and social problems of shelter utilization, we are aware that we have only peeked into a Pandora's Box of psychological difficulties involved with the atavistic return of man and his tribe to the recesses of the earth. It is one matter for man to have evolved from living deep in a Paleolithic cave to the city apartment or the garden home in the suburb, but an entirely different matter to consider whether he can successfully return to the cave. The question of whether an abrupt return along this evolutionary path is psychologically possible will hopefully remain a metaphysical issue.

Up to this point we have raised many questions, and it is appropriate that we suggest approaches to their solution that may have reasonable opportunity for success. It should be apparent that *prevention* of the need for a shelter program would be the best single approach to the social and psychological issues accompanying such a program. Like our public-health colleagues, who focus their attention on the malaria-producing swamp rather than on treatment of the individual patient, we should attempt to define the sources of the nuclear epidemic that we are now experiencing and thus to control it. The physician can accomplish this in part by fully assuming his professional responsibility for the preservation of human life. This emphasis on the biological approach may be effective in bringing into proper perspective the implications of such strategic concepts as "overkill" and the "toleration of 120,-000,000 deaths" in a first-strike nuclear raid.

One of the necessities in planning for a shelter program is reasonably adequate information about the magnitude of nuclear danger that confronts society. It appears that responsible government officials have been most cautious in communicating this information to the public for fear of arousing anxiety or apathy. Thus, the Office of Civil and Defense booklet[10] circulated recently gives survival information based on fallout effects of 5-megaton bombs, whereas blast, thermal and fallout effects of 20-megaton bomb attacks are more generally discussed in the official Holifield Committee hearings.[2] As physicians we may sympathize with this problem, since similar problems arise, for example, in deciding how much information a physician should communicate to a patient with a terminal cancer. As is well known, physicians take different views, which embrace a spectrum of positions ranging from that of telling the patient as little as possible to those who say that the patient must be told all. As psychiatrists we recognize that such communication must be tailored to meet the needs of a given patient. Although this analogy has obvious limitations there are many who see the present nuclear arms race as a type of malignant lesion encroaching upon the body politic, with the ever present possibility of metastatic dissemination of nuclear weapons.

Although the question of how much information should be communicated to the public is a difficult one, there is no question that the communication of misinformation or the lack of information is frequently more dangerous. As physicians we know that misinformation frequently leads to impairment of reality testing and results in maladaptive responses. Patients utilize diagnostic information according to their individual needs. Thus, some patients with cancer will deny its presence even when told of it and, by this denial, may bring about a situation where no corrective therapy is possible. On the other hand, there are patients who insist upon drastic and potentially life-shortening therapies. Still others turn to various forms of quackery. A very small proportion, through hopelessness and despondency, yield to self-destructive tendencies. Analogous to the last group are those who seek therapy for the cancer of nuclear threat through massive doses of radiation. As physicians we attempt to use judgment in adapting the type of therapy to the individual patient. We know that many can face the knowledge of life-threatening situations with a high degree of adaptive behavior, courage, and hope. Most people do seek out knowledge, make reasonable judgments and take action that is beneficial to themselves, their families, and their community.

Summary and Conclusions

We have attempted in this paper to delineate the nature of the situation that confronts man today in planning for his psychological and social survival under the threat of and in the event of a nuclear holocaust. We have quoted opinion and cited some anecdotal and laboratory observations that may be relevant to an understanding of these problems. We have suggested possible approaches physicians can make to some of these problems.

It is obvious that we have raised many more questions than we have answered. It should be apparent that the psychological and social problems raised in planning a defense-shelter program are of a magnitude and complexity that make it advisable to concentrate massive efforts on *eliminating the need* for such a program. Physicians, as one group of professionals concerned with the alleviation of suffering and the preservation of human life, are urged to examine the issues and take specific actions that will enable them most effectively to help prevent nuclear war.

References

1. United States Congress, Joint Committee on Atomic Energy. *Biological and environmental effects of nuclear war: Summary analysis of hearings, June 22-26, 1959.* 58 pp. Washington, D. C.: Government Printing Office, 1959.
2. Government Operations Committee, House. *Civil Defense, 1961: Hearings before a subcommittee, 87th Congress, 1st session, Aug. 1-9, 1961.* 554 pp. Washington, D. C.: Government Printing Office, 1961.
3. Bellamy, A. W. Stockpiling to survive a nuclear attack. *Science 138*: 958-960, 1962.
4. Baker, G. W., and Chapman, D. W. (Editors). *Man and Society in Disaster.* New York: Basic Books, 1962.

5. Baker, G. W. and Cottrell, L. S. (Editors). *Behavioral Science and Civil Defense. Disaster Study Number 16.* Disaster Research Group, National Academy of Sciences—National Research Council, Washington, D. C., 1962.

6. Science and human survival. *Science 134*:2080-2083, 1961.

7. *The Ranks of Death: A medical history of the conquest of America.* Edited by F. D. Asburn. 298 pp. New York: Coward-McCann, 1947.

8. Zinsser, H. *Rats, Lice and History: The biography of a bacillus.* 301 pp. Boston: Little, Brown, 1935.

9. Baldwin, H. Civil defense debate. *New York Times* (January 8), 1962. P. 33.

10. Department of Defense, Office of Civil and Defense Mobilization. *Fallout Protection, What to Know and Do About Nuclear Attack.* 46 pp. Washington, D. C.: Government Printing Office, December 30, 1961.

11. Krock, A. In the Nation. Shelters are from harsh reality. *New York Times* (January 2), 1962. P. 28.

12. Science, freedom and survival. *Am. A. Advancement Sc. Bull. 7*:2, 1962.

13. Escalona, S. *Children and the Threat of Nuclear War.* Child Study Association Publication. 27 pp. New York, 1962.

14. Hachiya, M. *Hiroshima Diary: The Journal of a Japanese physician, August 6-September 30, 1945.* Edited by W. Wells. 238 pp. Chapel Hill: Univ. North Carolina Press, 1955.

15. Nagai, T. *We of Nagasaki: The story of survivors in an atomic wasteland.* Translated by I. Shirato and H. B. L. Silverman. 189 pp. New York: Duell, 1951.

16. Janis, I. L. *Air War and Emotional Stress: Psychological studies of bombing and civilian defense.* 280 pp. New York: McGraw-Hill, 1951.

17. United States War Department, United States Strategic Bombing Survey. *Final Report, Covering Air-Raid Protection and Allied Subjects in Japan.* 243 pp. Washington, D. C.: Government Printing Office, 1947. (Forms No. 11, Pacific War.)

18. National Research Council and Army Medical Service Graduate School. *Symposium on Stress: Sponsored jointly by the Division of Medical Sciences, National Research Council, and Army Medical Service Graduate School, Walter Reed Army Medical Center.* 332 pp. Washington, D. C.: Government Printing Office, 1953.

19. Demerath, N. J. Symposium on adaptation to disaster, some general propositions: interpretative summary. *Human Organ. 16*:28, 1957.

20. Powell, J. W., Raynor, J., and Finesinger, J. E. Responses to disaster in American cultural groups. In National Research Council and Army Medical Service Graduate School.[18] Pp. 174-193.

21. Weybrew, B. B. Psychological and psychophysiological effects of long periods of submergence. I. Analysis of data collected during 265-hour, completely submerged, habitability cruise made by U.S.S. *Nautilus* (USN 571). Naval Medical Research Laboratory. (Report No. 281.) February 18, 1957. (Contents classified.)

22. Solomon, P., Leiderman, P. H., Mendelson, J. H., and Wexler, D. Sensory deprivation, review. *Am. J. Psychiat. 114*:357-363, 1957.

23. Bombard, A. *Voyage of the Hérétique.* 214 pp. New York: Simon & Schuster, 1953.

24. Byrd, R. E. *Alone*. 296 pp. New York: Putnam. 1938.
25. Leiderman, P. H., Mendelson, J. H., Wexler, D., and Solomon, P. Sensory deprivation: clinical aspects. *Arch. Int. Med. 101*:389-396, 1958.
26. *Sensory Deprivation: A symposium held at Harvard Medical School: Foreword by Stanley Cobb*. Edited by P. Solomon et al. 262 pp. Cambridge, Massachusetts: Harvard, 1961.
27. Office of Civil and Defense Mobilization. Vernon, J. A. *Project Hideaway: A pilot feasibility study of fallout shelters for families*. 35 pp. Washington, D. C.: Government Printing Office, December 2, 1959.
28. Frank, A. *The Diary of a Young Girl*. 285 pp. Garden City, New York: Doubleday, 1952.
29. Goldstein, B. *The Stars Bear Witness*. Edited by L. Shatzkin. 295 pp. New York: Viking, 1949.
30. Office of Civil and Defense Mobilization, American Institute for Research. Altman, J. W., et al. *Psychological and Social Adjustment in a Simulated Shelter, A Research Report*. 100 pp. Washington, D. C.: Government Printing Office, 1960.
31. West German Federal Civil Defense Agency. *Report on the Preparations for an Execution of an Air Raid Shelter Manning Test in "Shelter A" of the Waldbroel Federal Air Raid Protection School*. West Germany: Federal Civil Defense Agency, January, 1959.
32. Brand-Persson, A. Shelter programs and shelter occupancy experiments in Sweden. In National Academy of Sciences, National Research Council. *Symposium on Human Problems in the Utilization of Fallout Shelters: Held at the National Academy of Sciences, Washington, D. C., 11-12 February, 1960*. Edited by G. W. Baker et al. 234 pp. Washington, D. C.: The Council, 1960. Pp. 89-94.
33. United States Naval Radiological Defense Laboratory. Strope, W. E., et al. *Preliminary Report on Shelter Occupancy Test, December 3-17, 1959*. San Francisco, California: May 4, 1960.
34. Rohrer, J. B. Implications for fallout shelter living from studies of submarine habitability and adjustment to polar isolation. In National Academy of Sciences, National Research Council. *Symposium on Human Problems in the Utilization of Fallout Shelters: Held at the National Academy of Sciences, Washington, D. C., 11-12 February, 1960*. Edited by G. W. Baker et al. 234 pp. Washington, D. C.: The Council, 1960. Pp. 21-30.

The Illusion of Civil Defense

GERARD PIEL

TWO OMINOUS EVENTS—the testing of giant weapons in the Soviet Union and the sponsorship of fallout shelters by our own federal government—compel each one of us to contemplate thermonuclear war at close range. We have lived with the possibility of this calamity for more than a decade. We must now reckon with its probability.

No one, I suppose, will question my declaration that the Soviet Union, by resuming the testing of nuclear weapons, has increased the danger of war. I suspect, however, that I must document my charge that shelter-building in the U.S. also brings World War III closer. You should know at the outset that the documentation will compel us here and now to that close-range contemplation of thermonuclear war. When you have apprehended the nature of the war, I believe you will join me in the conclusion that civil defense is an illusion—an illusion that places our institutions and our lives in jeopardy.

The citizen who sets out to study thermonuclear war will find himself richly supplied with literature by his government. I have reviewed this material, and I must tell you that I find it to be incomplete and uneven in quality and reliability.

The hard facts at the foundation of this literature are the results of the weapons tests conducted by our government over the past 16 years—some 160 shots totaling about 120 megatons of explosive energy. In spite of the magnitude of the effort, these

57

experiments do not answer all our questions. For one thing, the results are not available to the citizen in their entirety. In the second place, these tests have been conducted in the wilderness of Nevada or on barren coral atolls in the South Pacific. They do not, therefore, tell us what a thermonuclear explosion would actually do to a crowded city at home—or to our forests and croplands. For direct demonstration of what might happen here we have only the experience with the nominal atomic bomb at Hiroshima and Nagasaki. But one quickly learns that experience with kiloton weapons has no direct application to the potential effects of weapons in the megaton range.

Quasi-Independent Consultants

On this limited, incomplete, and uncertain data there has grown a vast secondary literature. Here one finds the fruit of speculative investigations conducted by civil defense agencies, by the Atomic Energy Commission and the armed services, by certain academic institutions and individuals and by such quasi-independent organizations as the RAND Corporation working under contract for the armed services and other governmental agencies. Much of the material is conveniently packaged for reference in the proceedings of the several Congressional hearings on the biological and environmental effects of nuclear war and civil defense against those effects, proceedings that have made newspaper headlines during the past ten years.

Careful and critical reading of the secondary literature shows that the secondary investigations it reports are no less speculative for the fact that they have been conducted under the rubric of "operations research" and facilitated by the employment of large computers. It is evident that the assumptions fed into the computers heavily condition the results.

What the Client Wants to Hear

The work reported in this literature is threaded with two major strands of bias. One strong bias originates from the desire to envision and secure a significant civil defense. As one witness put it in the record of a Congressional hearing: ". . . we should always emphasize the survivors rather than the casualties . . . 'it is not what you have lost that is most important, but what you have left.' " This human tendency is entirely understandable in relation to the grave concerns of civil defense. Equally understandable is the pressure of bias that flows from the military contribution to the literature. One would expect military people to argue the validity of military solutions to political problems. It is perhaps less understandable—and surely less creditable—that their quasi-independent consultants should tell them what they want to hear. But you should not be surprised to learn the conclusion to which pressure from this quarter leads. This is that thermonuclear war is not only possible and probable but also feasible.

Now those who advance the feasibility of thermonuclear war do not claim that it is desirable. After living with the subject for more than a decade, however, these authors have learned not to shrink from horror. They face facts from which others recoil and distinguish between "a hopeless situation and a grim one," between a situation that "could be very serious" and yet "not catastrophic," between an "unprecedented catastrophe" and an "unlimited one." From close study of these distinctions they conclude that it is possible "to prevail in some meaningful sense of the term" if "not win."

In the calculus of feasibility, you must realize, civil defense plays a decisive role. Simple arithmetic shows it is the number of survivors that makes the difference between an unprecedented and an unlimited catastrophe. Here the objective of civil defense poses a delicate paradox. In all humanity, we must encourage measures that can save the lives of individuals. In the national interest, one must seek to minimize the number of casualties. But if such measures enhance the feasibility of thermonuclear war, then they may also raise the probability of war. At best, they increase the likelihood of unprecedented catastrophe. At worst, if the assumptions on which the civil defense measures are predicated prove to be wrong, they expose the nation and its people to unlimited catastrophe.

The basic doctrine of our national civil defense policy is a Spartan one. By now it is familiar to most of us: "In an atomic war, blast, heat, and initial radiation could kill millions close to ground zero of nuclear bursts. Many more millions—everybody else—could be threatened by radioactive fallout but most of these could be saved." No responsible official or consultant suggests that anyone can be protected against what are called the "prompt" effects of nuclear weapons: the initial radiation, heat, and blast. But people can be sheltered against fallout. It is against fallout, therefore, that the civil defense program is directed.

Even at this early stage of public indoctrination in civil defense, most people have learned to distinguish two kinds of fallout. There is, on the one hand, the fallout that has excited such concern during the recent series of Soviet tests and earlier during the last series of tests conducted by the U.S. This is the world-wide fallout that follows a test explosion in the atmosphere; the radioactive fission products are transported aloft by the fireball to be dissipated in the stratosphere and to return to earth later in high dilution and after great attenuation of their lethal energy.

Local Fallout

There is, on the other hand, the local fallout, which is of concern to civil defense. This fallout results when a nuclear weapon is burst on the ground. A major portion of the heat and blast energy is then transferred to the ground itself. The explosion scoops out a crater, and the fireball carries tons of vaporized and melted material from the ground upward in the air. The fission products are now trapped in particles of grit and dust as the material in the fireball cools and condenses. Secondarily, some of the material scooped from the crater is irradiated to add to the poisonous mass of the cloud. Only the finest particles carried upward in the fireball enter world-wide fallout. Some 80 per cent of the fission products fall out locally, the heaviest particles settling in a circle around the crater, the remainder riding on the wind to fall in high concentration on the ground downwind from ground zero.

This is the picture already engraved in the public imagination. There is a catastrophe at the target, as at Hiroshima and Nagasaki, from which few escape. There is local fallout from which those who are sheltered may escape.

With this picture in mind, most people are surprised to be reminded that there were no casualties from local fallout at Hiroshima or Nagasaki. The reason is that there was no local fallout in either of these catastrophes. As the President explained at the time, the two bombs were detonated at a height calculated to minimize the generation of local fallout. The President did not go on to explain that they were detonated at a height calculated to maximize the prompt effects of initial radiation, heat, and blast. These effects are suppressed by as much as 40 per cent in a ground burst in exchange for the radiological effects of local fallout or for the delivery of maximum ground shock to a hardened military target. Thus, as the saying goes in the vulgar lexicon of nuclear warfare: "You can't have everything, even when you've got an absolute weapon."

Emphasis on Fallout

Since fallout is the only effect that civil defense can cope with, you find the subject of fallout emphasized in civil defense. As one witness testified in June, 1959, before the Joint Committee on Atomic Energy: "Fallout and its potentially lethal areas are important, but so are the areas of the other effects; the pendulum of interest has swung to fallout and there is some tendency to overlook the very important other effects."

It stands to reason that, if a maximum number of people are to be protected against fallout, then a maximum number of people must be exposed to fallout in a given nuclear attack. Students of civil defense have given a great deal of time to the detailed investigations of hypothetical fallout attacks. In the June 1959 hearings, for example, experts from several agencies presented their findings on a hypothetical attack with a weight of about 1500 megatons directed against military and civilian targets in the continental U.S. All the 263 weapons employed in this attack on 224 targets were ground-burst. The computers, applying the ratios experienced at Hiroshima and Nagasaki, showed 30 million mortal casualties, plus 10 million surviving casualties caused by the prompt effects of these weapons. But they showed 10 million more killed and 10 million surviving injured as the result of exposure, without protection, to the effects of local fallout. The lesson of this study was that fallout shelters might have reduced mortal casualties by 25 per cent and the number of injured by half.

Even more dramatic results were reported at the hearings in August of this year [1961] by a subcommittee of the House Committee on Government Operations under the chairmanship of Representative Chet Holifield. The investigation covered a wide range of attacks, from 3,000 to 10,000 and on up to 30,000 megatons in total weight, directed primarily at military targets and employing air bursts instead of ground bursts only when the "softness" of the target permitted. The charts showed that, in the absence of civil defense precautions, total deaths might range from more than 10 per cent to substantially 100 per cent of the population, with casualties at the maximum when the entire weight of the attack was committed to ground bursts. With fallout shelters affording somewhat less protection than those envisioned in the present civil defense program, these figures were shown to be reduced by as much as 40 per cent. With more substantial fallout shelters that would also afford "nominal protection against blast," the study showed more than 90 per cent of the population surviving the 3,000 megaton attack and as much as 60 per cent surviving the 30,000 megaton attack.

Such figures certainly come down with heavy weight on the side of preparing substantial fallout shelters. But the witness who reported on these figures was careful to moderate their impact. He pointed out that ". . . the outcomes of future attacks are anything but precisely predictable. Fallout could create overwhelming disaster, but it might not." And he added: ". . . it depends most importantly on the kind of war the combatants may be prepared to fight."

We shall return to this question of the kinds of war the combatants may fight in a moment. The feasibility of thermonuclear war involves another big question that I should like to consider with you now:

If fallout shelters can secure a substantial number of survivals, what kind of world will they survive into? As Governor Rockefeller's Committee on Fallout Protection defines the problem: "There are many unsettled questions as to what people should do, where they should go, to whom they should look when it is safe to leave shelters."

The answers to these questions are somewhat less precisely predictable than the casualty rate. But they have been subjected to study, and the recuperation of the nation from at least one of the possible wars has been projected in a preliminary way.

Skipping the question of whether the weight of the attack was given to military or civilian targets and whether casualties were caused by ground bursts or air bursts, we are confronted with the aftermath of a war that has devastated the 53 largest metropolitan regions of the U.S. A third of the population has been killed, half of our industrial capacity destroyed.

When it comes to recuperation, however, we must look to what is left: two-thirds of the population and half of the nation's industrial capacity. It turns out, furthermore, that we have lost the more expendable portion of our total country—the "A" country composed of the principal metropolitan regions, as compared with the "B" country of lesser cities and rural countryside. "It further turns out that . . . while the A country cannot survive without a B country, the B country cannot only survive without the A country; it also seems to have the resources and skills to rebuild the A country in about 10 years."

Recuperation

The achievement of such a rate of recovery, however, depends on the assumption "that extensive reorganization could be accomplished within perhaps six months." According to the report, "the initial phase of economic activity . . . would be dominated by reorganization problems . . . Some of the problems are physical, such as the patching up of capital that has suffered only partial damage (for example, electric power grids, open-hearth furnaces without chimneys), decontamination of factories immobilized by fallout, and even the disposal of millions of dead. Other pressing problems are institutional: preservation of the governmental framework, restoration of the monetary system and of decision-making authority in business enterprises, re-establishment of markets for consumer goods and raw materials (though doubtless controlled in certain respects), and activation of the labor force so that people support themselves by regular work (often in new occupations)." The projected recuperation also assumes that the people would not have sustained any long-term psychological disability from their experience, that the human germ plasm would tolerate a prolonged exposure to levels of background radiation far above the present level and that the environment would not have received any permanent ecological damage.

It is conceded that these questions require deeper study. Recuperation economics, for example, involves some distressing variations on the familiar Malthusian equation. One student has testified: ". . . the relative balance between surving population and surviving productive capacity has a very important bearing on the problem of economic recuperation. . . . [A] situation could easily arise where the surviving wealth per capita was greater than it is now. . . . [On] the other hand . . . most of our population may survive . . . but the destruction of productive capacity may make it difficult to support the survivors in the long run. Thus the relative importance of the problems of recovery may be inversely related to the level of direct population casualties in the war."

"The Dominating Questions"

Still other questions remain to be studied. One expert has termed these "the social, psychological, political, and moral problems of recuperation" and has said "these . . . are currently the hard questions. Many feel they are the dominating questions."

With all these questions remaining to be studied, it is to be doubted that the nation as a whole has accepted the feasibility of thermonuclear war. Whether the [Kennedy] Administration has adopted this thesis I do not know. One may suppose the prevailing view is that the test of this hypothesis may not be made at our choice. In any case, the first steps in preparation for the experiment have now been taken. The federal government has launched a $200-million program to survey, mark, and supply 20 million fallout shelter spaces in the central cities. The President has personally encouraged citizens to build fallout shelters on their own premises and to stock them for a two-week stay. Going beyond the results from the computers, the popularizers of the program promise that 97 per cent will be saved.

In the President's judgment, the sole function of the present program is to save the lives that can be saved. Civil defense, he said, "cannot deter a nuclear attack." There is some dissent from this narrow concept. Speaking for a great many military minds, General Lyman L. Lemnitzer has said "civil defense is a part of our total deterrent," in the sense that capacity to survive and recuperate is calculated to deter the enemy from striking first. Still a third position is advanced by some academic and quasi-academic experts on thermonuclear war; they prefer to believe that civil defense will lend credibility to our nuclear arsenal, giving it what they call "First-Strike Credibility" based on our capacity to sustain a counterattack.

"Here Was the End of War"

In the present atmosphere, it is difficult to recall that 16 years ago the atomic scientists had proved war is obsolete as a means for arbitrating international political disputes. They did their best at the time to put this understanding across. As Harold Urey pointed out, "atomic bombs don't land in the next block, leaving survivors to thank their lucky stars and . . . to hope the next bomb will also miss them." Urey and other scientists "thought the possibilities would be so apparent that when humanity saw what science had done, they would see immediately that here was the end of war." Since 1945 there has been no fundamental change in the physics that underlies this conclusion. No basic discovery has made thermonuclear war either more violent or more feasible. Long before Alamogordo, Urey's heavy-water process had made the heavy isotopes of hydrogen abundantly available. The hydrogen bomb was implicit in the fission bomb. All that was needed was the technology that has come along simultaneously and independently in the U.S. and the U.S.S.R. and in other countries as well.

To recapture the mood of the nuclear physicists we must take a still closer look at what happens in a nuclear explosion. We shall see that the escalation from kilotons to megatons requires reconsideration of the premises of civil defense. The nominal atomic bomb that terminated World War II is said to have had the destructive power of 20 kilotons of TNT. At Hiroshima the TNT-equivalent blast effect leveled a roughly circular area one mile in radius. The blast effect in this case overrode and obscured the consequences of the other two prompt effects of the nuclear explosion. In the first instant of detonation, the bomb had showered the same area of one-mile radius with a lethal pulse of high-energy radiation. This is the "initial radiation" referred to in civil defense literature. During the next few seconds the fireball evolved and showered the same area of one-mile radius with thermal energy sufficient to ignite fires and inflict third-degree burns on all human beings directly exposed within one mile of ground zero.

Decreasing Relevance of TNT

The destructive capacity of still larger weapons is expressed on the same scale of TNT-equivalent explosive power. But this scale has decreasing relevance to the true nature of these weapons as they grow larger. The ranges of the three prompt effects —initial radiation, heat, and blast—increase at different rates with increase in size. This is to say that the three concentric circles of destruction and lethality that were coterminous at Hiroshima increase at significantly different rates as technology packs more violence into the nuclear warhead. The initial-radiation circle increases most slowly because this radiation is absorbed and scattered, and it falls so far within the other two that it may be ignored. The circle of total destruction by blast grows faster; its radius increases as the cube root of the increase in TNT-equivalent tonnage. But the circular area showered with thermal radiation grows the fastest of all; its radius increases as the square root of the increase in power. Thus the area engulfed in the incendiary effects of the bigger weapons reaches outward far beyond the perimeter of the blast circle.

Square Root of the Increase

The analysis on page xiii shows that the 20-megaton bomb, 1,000 times bigger than the 20-kiloton bomb, has a blast radius of 10 miles (the cube root of 1,000) and an incendiary radius of 30 miles (the square root of 1,000). By the same token, the 50-megaton bomb tested in the Soviet Union must have a blast radius of about 13 miles but an incendiary radius of 50; a 100-megaton bomb would have a blast radius of about 17 miles and an incendiary radius of 70. If 100, why not 1,000 megatons? Such a weapon would have an incendiary radius of 200 miles.

The conclusion to be comprehended here is that the bigger the weapon is, the more preponderantly it becomes an incendiary weapon. There are two decisive elements in the incendiary effect of the big weapon. The first is that the ignition of many fires at once throughout the 3,000 square miles around a 20-megaton burst is sure to produce a gigantic single fire, a conflagration so huge that it must be reckoned as a meteorological event—a fire storm. The blast effect would destroy the central city, but the fire storm would incinerate the metropolitan area.

The Fire Storm

Not much is said about fire storms in the literature of thermonuclear war and civil defense. For perfectly obvious reasons, the effect is not one of those subjected to experimental study in the long series of weapons tests. There was some experience with fire storms ignited by ordinary incendiary bombs in World War II: the fire storm at Dresden is estimated to have killed 300,000 people in a single night; at Hamburg, some 70,000; at Tokyo, some

200,000. Blastproof bomb shelters afforded no protection in these storms; their occupants were found suffocated and cremated when the shelters were opened. The fire storm at Hiroshima burned inside the perimeter of the blast effect.

This brings us to the second decisive element in the incendiary effect of the giant weapons. That is the so-called perimeter-to-area ratio: as the radius of the circle increases, the area within goes up as the square of the increase, and the edge of the fire storm moves farther and farther away from ground zero. A number of people at Hiroshima who had been sheltered from blast and heat escaped from inside the circle of destruction before the fire storm took over. It was this experience, programed into the computers, that moderated the casualty estimates in the 1500-megaton ground-burst attack postulated at the 1959 hearings of the Joint Committee. A far smaller percentage of the population would escape from the vast interior of a 20-megaton fire storm.

Up to this point I have not mentioned fallout in connection with these big weapons. The reason is, of course, that the fire and especially the blast effect of these weapons are maximized by air-burst, by detonating them in the atmosphere high off the ground at altitudes proportioned to the size of the particular weapon and its fireball. Under these circumstances there is no local fallout. A 20-megaton weapon can, of course, be ground-burst. But it would not be profitable to use such a weapon for its radiological effects, because the square mileage destroyed by its incendiary effect already approximates the area that could be covered by intense fallout. The same logic applies with increasing force to still larger weapons.

Six Western States

In each case the incendiary effect can be magnified still further in exchange for blast effect by bursting the bigger weapons at very high altitude. Since most of the atmosphere lies closer to the ground, there is little loss of energy, and the cone of effective thermal radiation gains a still wider radius at its base. According to one set of calculations, a 1000-megaton bomb detonated at satellite altitude could set six Western—Western, not Middle Western—states afire.

It is evident from the literature that no adequate consideration has been given to the incendiary aspect of thermonuclear war.

Fire was not mentioned, for example, in connection with the fall-out shelters that were supposed to provide "nominal protection against blast" in the model fallout attacks described at the Holifield hearings in August. Yet any blast effect would be felt well inside the fire storm. It was admitted at those hearings that there has been no research on "what might be called the environmental fire problem," that is, the burning of forests, prairies and croplands. It may be that the fire storm is, indeed, unthinkable.

Throughout the literature it is implied that people and property outside the bull's-eye are safe from fire as well as blast. All *they* have to worry about, one gathers, is fallout. The fact is that the only thing they *can* worry about is fallout.

With public anxiety thus directed to fallout, the Administration's civil defense program promises fallout protection. The federal effort to establish fallout shelters in the central cities will provide such protection if fallout is the hazard to which the population is exposed. If not, these shelters will trap the urban populations in blast and fire. Concurrently, the individual citizen is urged to provide for himself the fallout "protection best suited to his needs." The 60 per cent of the population that has basements readily accessible to it is advised to install a "basement shelter [that] can be built with solid concrete blocks as a do-it-yourself project" for $150 to $200. Again, such a shelter will provide protection if fallout (of the estimated intensity) is the only hazard to which its occupants are exposed. Within the incendiary radius of a big bomb, however, the basement shelter becomes a firetrap.

Other Worries

Even with fallout as the strategic hazard, there are other things to worry about. At the August hearing on civil defense an expert presented this portrait of a householder standing on his own property "about 25 miles from an important, somewhat isolated strategic target." The target comes under a 20-megaton ground burst. "Survival depends on how much this man has found out about weapons effects, about the precautions he needs to take, and above all what he has actually done. For instance, a shelter with a shielding factor of 100 makes the radiation tolerable. Because of the slower rate of delivery of thermal energy from the high-yield weapons, he can reduce effectively the number of calories hitting him if he ducks behind something opaque. After a few seconds the bulk of the thermal energy will have been emitted and he then has about 2 minutes to get to a place where he'll be safe from flying glass and other missiles created by the blast wave which travels at the speed of sound. Depending on the meteorological conditions, of course, the fallout could be expected to arrive in around 20 minutes to an hour and continue to fall for about 2 to 6 hours. Thus it can be seen that the effects of a detonation of 20 megatons as experienced at 25 miles do not confront our man simultaneously. If he knows the sequence of events, and if he knows what he has to do to survive, he has time to act. He does have to act correctly the first time or take the consequences.

"At such distances few knowledgeable, intelligent people need be hurt seriously."

"Burns to the Retina"

It is necessary to add, from the testimony of the same witness, that this man must take care not to look at the fireball as it comes above the horizon: ". . . experiments during the tests above Johnston Island in 1958 show that burns to the retina can occur as far away as . . . 345 statute miles." One must mention also that "the possibility of direct thermal radiation being transmitted by re-radiation into a shelter" is still under investigation.

The idea that fallout constitutes the principal hazard to the civilian population is a derivation from military theory. Remembering Pearl Harbor, our military thinkers are convinced that the enemy will lay the primary weight of his attack on our military installations. We have the word from General Curtis E. LeMay, who commanded the 20th Air Force in our strike against Hiroshima and Nagasaki: "There is no point in going after the civilian population as such." The first attack by the enemy would therefore be what is called a "counterforce" attack, directed at the destruction of our capacity to retaliate. With a substantial portion of our retaliatory force installed in hardened missile bases, the enemy warheads would necessarily be ground-burst, and the civilian population would accordingly come under heavy fallout as a side effect.

300-Megaton Fallout

To be effective the weight of this attack would have to be considerable. An independent study by a meteorologist at the University of Arizona shows that 300 megatons would have to be laid in a few minutes on the 18 hardened Titan bases that ring the city of Tucson. The same considerations apply apparently to other communities where missile bases have been installed within logistically convenient range: Wichita and Salina, Kansas; Little Rock, Arkansas; the Rome-Utica complex in New York; Lincoln, Nebraska; Altus, Oklahoma; Abilene, Texas; and Plattsburgh, New York, among others. With heavy ground-burst attacks directed at such targets, the nearby communities would come under fallout of intensities far above those against which the do-it-yourself basement shelter, supplied for two weeks of refuge, could afford protection. Apparently the siting of missile bases has considerably depressed the prospects of country B. With the distribution of other targets more nearly approximating that of the economy and the population as a whole, one can see the logic in Admiral Arleigh A. Burke's declaration that "in general nuclear war missile forces can no longer attempt to destroy their enemy's counterpart without destroying the corporate body of the enemy state itself. . . ."

"Counterforce Plus Bonus"

The elaborate studies of the fallout hazard can be set aside entirely if the attacker should choose to attack the population directly instead of by side effect. As the expert who presented the hypothetical 30,000-megaton fallout attack at the August civil defense hearing said: "So far as initial impact of any attack is concerned, the level of fatalities is extremely sensitive to attack design." The attacker could, for example, adopt the strategy of "counterforce plus bonus." By diverting 10 per cent of the 30,000 megatons, or 3,000 megatons, to civilian targets he could, according to this witness, "kill as many as 120 million people." He would take as his bonus the substantially complete destruction of U.S. civilization. The population is a soft target and, as such, highly vulnerable to prompt effects. It takes fewer megatons to kill the corporate body of the state than to destroy the forces that are supposed to defend it.

Rational Strategies

Civil defense, it is said, "increases markedly our ability to survive war if [the war] is fought by rational methods." But there is little reason to think that a real war will be fought by the rational strategies of game theory that are supplied as inputs to a computer. The experience of history suggests that the first exchange, if "rational," will trigger an unlimited escalation of violence, going on to the final exhaustion and destruction of the installed capacity for violence. We must remember Hiroshima as well as Pearl Harbor.

Not only the U.S. and the U.S.S.R. but also their allies and satellites and the neutrals in line of fire face the same dread prospect. We are assured that the empty world of *On the Beach* is pure fiction. But the fire storms of a thermonuclear war could work an irreversible disruption of the social and moral fabric of Western civilization. The kind of society that would emerge from the shelters may be guessed from the kind of society that is preparing to go into shelters now.

Escalation to Catastrophe

The escalation toward the ultimate catastrophe is already under way. We are passing from an era of research and development into an era of intercontinental push-button armaments in readiness for action. The major thermonuclear powers will soon have others in their Jovian company. There will be bigger weapons and more of them, and earth satellites as well as rockets to deliver them. Across the continents and under the oceans, the weapons will be deployed in ever larger number and variety. The danger of the totally irrational accidental war must mount as control over these weapons becomes attenuated over constantly lengthening chains of command.

We are personally witness to this escalation, in the rising tide of callousness and brutality here at home. It is to be seen, at the top level of our government, in the writing off of Tucson and other cities by the siting of missile bases in their immediate environs. It erupts in an ugly way, at the middle level, in the vigilante league of Las Vegas and Bakersfield against the prospective flood of refugees from Los Angeles. It shames our people before the world in the climax of American privatism that prescribes a sawed-off shotgun as equipment for the family fallout shelter.

The civil defense program of our federal government, however else intended, must be regarded as a step in the escalation process. This is a sinister development because it works a psychological subversion of both government and citizenry. It gives the sanction of action to the delusion that a thermonuclear war can be fought and survived. It encourages statesmen to take larger risks predicated on First-Strike Credibility and Post-Attack Recuperative Capacity. It disengages the citizen from vigilance over the rationality and responsibility of his elected officials.

On the other side of the world power contest, in satisfaction of the equations of war-game theory, it invites a Pre-emptive Strike. For the dubious protection it promises, civil defense has exacted a dangerous cost to national security.

It is clear that, in launching its fallout-shelter program, the Administration has sought to find a compromise. Between the still overwhelming popular reluctance to accept violence as a way of life on the one hand and the pressure to "do something" on the other, the Administration has cut its problem down the middle.

Pressure From Two Quarters

The Administration has yielded to pressure from essentially two quarters. The first originates with irresponsible politicians in both parties who have adopted fallout defense as a mode of political dynamism. The second and much more significant pressure originates with the military and its commitment to military solutions, backed by the powerful economic interest in those solutions that has come to be the biggest business in the land. But a primary responsibility for this hoax on public opinion must be attributed to those authors of fraud by computer who produced the literature that argues the feasibility of thermonuclear war.

The Administration's purchase of this hoax raises two grim possibilities. First, it may have seriously compromised its capacity to rally public opinion in favor of the settlements it is seeking to negotiate at the conference table. Second, in the mood of mounting fear and truculence, the Administration may find it has provoked demagogic clamor for a civil defense program going far beyond the present one.

The Underground Society

Such programs have been studied and estimated in a preliminary way. The down payment on the cost of taking the nation underground would be $150 billion. But that is only the fiscal cost. The social cost of going underground would not fall short of the total transformation of our way of life, the suspension of our civil institutions, the habituation of our people to violence and the ultimate militarization of our society. By that time it would surely be difficult to define the ideological conflict that the war is supposed to be fought about. And by that time the technology of thermonuclear war will no doubt be equal to hunting out its targets underground.

If this analysis suggests that a third alternative to the choice of surrender or death may be found in the Garrison State, let me urge a fourth alternative. We must accept the truth that thermonuclear war cannot settle even the most irreconcilable conflict to anybody's satisfaction. With all due caution, at the present stage in the escalation of terror, we must seek the settlement of political differences by peaceful means. Concurrently we must seek an immediate halt in the arms race and thereafter general and complete disarmament under controls that will protect mankind from its resumption. The two elements are inseparable; for it is clear that there would be no German problem if we had disarmament and that there can be no convention on disarmament that does not include China.

The Continuation of History

History has lagged behind the progress of technology, and now an unprecedented emergency confronts the continuation of history. The conflicts that hang over from the good old pre-thermonuclear days cannot be arbitrated by war. They must be settled before madness, stupidity, accident, or the arms race itself precipitates the war. If we enter into negotiation in distrust and fear of the other party, we must bear in mind that the other party bears the same distrust and fear of us. If we think they lack our sophisticated appreciation of the menace of thermonuclear weapons, let us recall that they have fresh in memory their 25 million dead of World War II. Both sides are driven to the conference table by the same iron compulsion that flows from the thermonuclear inversion of the Golden Rule.

The Biology of Nuclear War

BENTLEY GLASS, PH.D.

How Big a War?

ALL SORTS of magnitude have been envisaged for nuclear wars, ranging from minor, limited uses of such tactical weapons as a single man may carry and fire from a bazooka, to the world-wide devastation and fallout that might result if enemy powers were to launch 30,000 megatons of nuclear weapons at each other. The first question that must be answered, in a discussion of the effects of nuclear war upon living things is, simply: "How big a war?"

A second question is of almost equal importance, though it presupposes that the nuclear war will not be of a magnitude that is all-destroying. This question involves the strategy employed by the military forces in their selection of targets. Will the nuclear weapons be aimed solely at the striking force, the "counterforce" of the enemy, that is, at its missile launching sites, its intercontinental bomber bases, and its other retaliatory forces? Or, on the contrary, will the weapons be aimed at the cities and industrial plants, the communication centers and the hubs of transportation of the opponent? The choice of one of these alternatives matters immensely, since the patterns of destruction from blast, fire, and high-energy radiation will differ exceedingly depending upon the location of the targets within a country.

It is consequently necessary for us to define and delimit our consideration of the problem by making tentative answers to these questions even though we must keep in mind that the problems we explore and the conclusions we reach may be very different if different assumptions about the magnitude and the strategy of nuclear warfare be chosen. In the hearings on the *Biological and Environmental Effects of Nuclear War* held by the Joint Committee on Atomic Energy of the United States Congress in 1959, an attack on the United States of 263 weapons delivered on 224 targets, and amounting to 1,446 megatons of explosive power distributed in weapons of 1, 2, 3, 8, and 10 megatons each was assumed as a basis for the calculation of effects. No specific reasons for assuming this magnitude of attack were given, but the description of the exercise indicates that an attack of this size would be sufficient to blanket the principal military counterforce targets in the United States. Included were 111 Air Force installations, 71 critical target areas (centers of population and industry), 21 AEC installations, 12 Army installations, 5 Navy installations, and 4 Marine Corps installations. The assumed attack was thus not directed *primarily* at population centers. For purposes of calculating the world-wide fallout, it was assumed that the attack on the United States was matched by the detonation of 2500 megatons elsewhere, so that the total fallout would result from the explosion of approximately 4000 megatons of nuclear weapons. It was further assumed that 50 per cent of the explosive power would be derived from fission and the other half from fusion, and that the radioactive products would be derived entirely from the fission reactions. This was at a time before it was recognized that the carbon-14 produced by the fusion process would constitute a considerable and very long-lasting portion of the total fallout.

Already in 1959 some of the effects of much larger attacks than the one assumed for the hearings had been calculated in various studies. One paper, reprinted in full in the published volume on the hearings, in fact calculates the casualties and deaths to be expected in "unprepared" contrasted with "prepared," that is, adequately sheltered, populations for attacks up to a level of 50,000 megatons.[1] It seems probable that the much smaller magnitude of the postulated attack was dictated partly by the minimal size of attack needed to destroy the prime targets, and partly by the desire not to alarm the general public by imagining an attack of far greater dimensions. It did not reckon with the need to allow for misses, and it was apparently not related to the existing stockpiles of nuclear weapons and the delivery capacities of the opponents, which are far greater than are needed to mount 1500-megaton attacks. These points seem to have been realized in planning the 1961 hearings before the House Committee on Government Operations, for on the later occasion a wide range of attacks, from 3000 up to 30,000 megatons, was postulated.

The casualties and destruction resulting from even a "small" 1500-megaton attack on an unsheltered population are appalling. The 1959 hearings predicted that deaths would amount to 42 million persons in the 71 critical target areas, or 27.8 per cent of the 1950 population on which the estimates were based. In addition, 17.2 million survivors would be injured. The same "modest" attack would produce today—under the same conditions, since no real increase in effective shelters has been produced—over 51 million dead and 21 million injured. Yet we cannot assume that even these figures represent a reasonable estimate of the disaster.

One strategy of attack assumes that the blow will be strictly against the retaliatory power of the victim. Another, however, assumes that the primary target will include the general population and the industrial centers of the enemy. It is hard to suppose that once combat has been initiated the disorder and failure of communications, together with the uncontrollable emotions which can be foreseen, will not lead to an all-out attack. One may also with reason ask why the United States continues to construct atomic-powered submarines armed with Polaris missiles, as a major item of defense. The Polaris missile does not exceed 1-megaton in magnitude and is neither sufficiently accurate, we are informed, to be used against small targets like hardened missile-launching sites, nor sufficiently powerful to destroy them except by a direct hit. But the Polaris missiles are a potent deterrent against enemy nuclear attack, nevertheless, for they pose the threat of the destruction of cities and industrial areas. Nor is it reasonable to suppose that, in the anticipation of a nuclear attack upon the SAC bases of this country, the military commanders would not deploy forces and thus make of every commercial airport for jet planes a logical target. These airports, of course, are in close proximity to all our major cities. Cities are also the communication and transportation hubs of a nation; and if the enemy would have reason to suppose that a first strike might not annihilate the counterforce and that a second counterstrike might be expected, then every center of communications would become a logical target. It seems hard not to agree with General Lauris Norstad, commander in chief of NATO, when he said before Congress:

> I do not agree with those people who say you can control the size of this fire, the size of this blast, neatly, cold-bloodedly, once it starts. I think it is the most dangerous and disastrous thing in the world. I think you must prevent the thing from starting in the first place, because once it starts in a critical area such as the NATO area, it is more likely than not, in my opinion, to explode into the whole thing, whether we like it or the Russians like it or anybody likes it.[2]

It seems more reasonable, then, to consider the possibility of a nuclear war that would strike both at the counterforce and at the population, one that would attempt to deal so crushing a first blow that no second strike in return would be possible. Considering that present missiles carry nuclear warheads only up to 5 megatons in power, and that old-fashioned bombers can deliver up to 20 megatons apiece, besides being far more numerous than the available missiles, we may conclude that at least for some years to come great bomber fleets will constitute the primary delivery threat, supplemented, to be sure, by such missiles as are ready. It would require only 1000 bombers, each carrying a 20-megaton bomb, to deliver an attack of 20,000 megatons. We may assume that the stockpiles of bombs are ample, for public statements have been made regarding the size of our own stockpile that place it considerably in excess of that figure. Let us also assume that no more than half the carriers of bombs—missiles and planes—reach enemy territory and explode their charges on it or over it. That is a far more conservative assumption than the actuality of World War II, when about 90 per cent of bombers delivered their loads on the target areas. We thus come to the conclusion that a 10,000-megaton attack on either side, or a total 20,000-megaton exchange, is not unlikely if nuclear war does occur; and that the United States is far more likely to be hit with 10,000 megatons than with 1500 megatons of nuclear bombs. An estimated 300 megatons assigned for the destruction of each of about 20 missile launching sites, and considerably less per SAC base, might require perhaps 7000 megatons for the strike against the launching sites of our counterforce. The remainder, some 3000 megatons, is between five and six times the level of attack assumed in the 1959 hearings to be directed against the 71 critical target areas, representing the major concentrations of population and industry in the country, and ranging in size from New York City down to York, Pennsylvania.

From the calculations previously referred to, we can now calculate the probable deaths according to various geographic distributions of the detonations and upon the assumption that fission and fusion are equal. Everett and Pugh assumed that the fission yield was two-thirds of the total yield; but bombs are "cleaner" now. A relatively unprepared population would then stand to lose about 82 per cent of its numbers by death within 60 days, and a total of 90 per cent casualties if the density of the yield was proportional to the distribution of the population; or 60 per cent deaths within 60 days and a total of 78 per cent casualties if the yield density was proportional to the distribution of military airbases. These figures provide us with limits. Perhaps an intermediate figure is more realistic: about 130 million dead within 60 days, and 25 million additional casualties. That is to say, of the 50 million survivors about half would be seriously injured. Furthermore, as Everett and Pugh state, the casualties at 60 days are not the full toll of ultimate casualties. "Such delayed effects as the disorganization of society, disruption of communications, extinction of livestock, genetic damage, and the slow development of radiation poisoning from the ingestion of radioactive materials may significantly increase the ultimate toll."

In the U.S.S.R., because the area of the country is so much greater and so much of it is sparsely inhabited, the effects of a similar attack would be somewhat lessened. Nevertheless, 62 to 70 per cent of the population would die within 60 days after a 10,000-megaton attack.

Biological Effects of Nuclear Explosions

The destructive effects of nuclear detonations result from blast, thermal radiation (heat), and high-energy radiation (comparable to x-rays). Radioactive particles are also produced, carried up by the fireball, and distributed to a distance. These, when they descend, constitute the fallout. It is interesting, and probably surprising to most persons, to learn that no one was killed at Hiroshima or Nagasaki from fallout. Those 20-kiloton bombs, puny by modern standards, burst in the air, and the one-mile radius of their blast and incendiary effects extended as far from the hypocenter (directly under the point of detonation) as did their radiation effects.

Air bursts produce relatively little radioactive material in comparison with surface bursts, and a 20-kiloton bomb does not release sufficient energy for the fireball to rise into the stratosphere and achieve world-wide distribution. Nor was there significant local fallout, beyond the area of blast and heat damage. Fallout, in fact, came into the world as a virtually new phenomenon when weapons tests of megaton bombs began in 1952.

The biological effects of nuclear war would involve the several effects of blast, heat, direct radiation, and fallout. From bombs of moderate size, up to 1 megaton, damage to living things is equally from blast and from heat. Above that size, the radius of damage from fire storm increases more rapidly than that from blast. For a 20-kiloton bomb, each radius is about one mile, as already mentioned; but for a 20-megaton bomb, the blast radius of which is 10 miles, the incendiary radius is 30 miles; for a 50-megaton bomb, the blast radius is 13 miles but the incendiary radius is 50 miles; and for the latest giant, the 100-megaton bomb, the blast radius is 17 miles but the incendiary radius is 70 miles. The blast radius increases as the cube root of the energy in megatons, but the incendiary radius increases as the square root. Gerard Piel puts it tersely: "The blast effect would destroy the central city, but the fire storm would incinerate the metropolitan area." [3] Consequently, for large airburst bombs, the principal danger is that of fire and fire storm. The latter occurs when raging conflagrations over great areas so deplete the air of its oxygen that much carbon monoxide is produced. In World War II, in the great fire storms produced by old-fashioned incendiary bombs in Dresden, Hamburg, and Tokyo, far greater loss of life occurred than in Hiroshima or Nagasaki. The deaths were estimated at 300,000 in Dresden, 70,000 in Hamburg, and 200,000 in Tokyo. Here the occupants of bomb shelters were found suffocated and cremated in their places of refuge. The plain lesson is that shelters, to be effective in a metropolitan area, must be more than blastproof. They must be completely sealable and heatproof, and provided with means of supplying adequate oxygen and removal of carbon dioxide for periods of 24 hours or more. Fallout is simply not the problem in the primary target areas.

Large bombs burst on the ground or in the water are another matter. From ground-burst bombs the main danger is from the fire storm, up to the limits of the incendiary radius. Beyond that distance, the danger is from the local fallout, composed of the heavier particles of radioactive material that are produced by the bomb-burst and that settle out relatively quickly. These are particles from the size of cinders down to the size of ordinary house dust. Crooked air intakes for the shelters will keep out the bigger ones, and furnace or air-conditioner filters will eliminate most of the dust-sized particles, as most of us know from everyday experience.

The fallout contains radioactive isotopes of many sorts, some with relatively short half-lives, some with very long ones. Thus iodine-131, which has a half-life of 8 days, is reduced in one month to less than 10 per cent of its original amount, and in 8 months to less than 1 per cent of the original amount. Though short-lived, iodine-131 is particularly dangerous because it is concentrated by the human body in the thyroid gland, where its radiation may kill some or all of the cells of the gland and produce serious or fatal consequences. Strontium-90 and cesium-137 last longer, their half-lives being respectively 28 and 30 years. Strontium-90, resembling calcium in its chemical properties, is stored like calcium in the bones of the body. Here it emits beta rays of low penetration (about 1 centimeter), so that strontium-90 constitutes a hazard primarily to the bone cells and the bone marrow. Bone cancer and possibly leukemia might result, though neither would arise until long after the passage of the 60 days used earlier in reckoning the deaths and casualties attributable to nuclear war. Cesium-137 seeks out no particular tissue, but it emits highly penetrating gamma rays as well as beta rays. It thus constitutes more of a hazard to the entire body, including the reproductive organs where the cells reside that harbor the hereditary materials which will endow future generations. Fortunately, whereas strontium-90 is likely to stay in the skeleton for years or even a lifetime, cesium-137 moves rather quickly through the body, with an average biological residence of only 17 days.

Carbon-14 must also be mentioned. Unlike the other radioactive isotopes already described, this one occurs naturally, being formed in the upper atmosphere by cosmic ray bombardment. Also unlike the others mentioned, it is formed by nuclear fusion rather than fission. What has been formed by nuclear explosions to date about equals the amount normally present in the atmosphere, and is far less (about one-eightieth) than the amount present in the ocean, in plants, and in the air. We might therefore neglect this small increment as being of little importance, were it not for two things. First, carbon-14 has a very long half-life of 5600 years, so that whatever is produced by man's nuclear explosions will steadily accumulate over thousands of years. Secondly, though the biological residence of carbon-14 is only 6 months on the average, it can become incorporated into the very molecules of deoxyribose nucleic acid (DNA) which form the genes. When such an atom of carbon-14 disintegrates, it produces the destruction or gross alteration of the molecule of which it was a part. In hereditary terms, this means that the gene is lost or mutates, generally to a form that produces damage in some descendant.

The local fallout, because of irregularities of the wind, usually assumes the form of a twisted plume extending downwind from the point of detonation. In the case of a large bomb, it may extend 150 miles downwind and 50 miles across. The fallout is of course heavier in the center of this plume than toward the edges or the tip. In the case of a 10,000-megaton war, these plumes of fallout would virtually blanket the country, especially the area lying east of the Mississippi River. The intensity of radiation from the fallout drops off with surprising rapidity, roughly tenfold for every sevenfold increase in time. After six months, it drops off even faster. Thus, as calculated by Ralph Lapp,[4] a dose rate of 4000 roentgens per hour for the first hour following a detonation will drop to 2500 r/hr during the second hour and 550 r/hr during the fifth hour. The total for the first day would amount to 12,150 r, but for the second day it would drop to 950 r. By the fourth day the total dose for the day would no longer exceed the median lethal dose for human beings. On the seventh day, with a mean dose rate of only 5 r/hr, the total dose for the day would be 120 r. At this level it would be safe for a person to stay outdoors and unsheltered for a considerable time, provided the total dose accumulated did not exceed certain limits. Even an initial dose rate many times higher than that assumed in these calculations would require only a very few additional hours to drop to the first level postulated here. Moreover, higher initial dose rates may be largely ignored, since they will occur only inside the radius of total destruction by blast and fire.

For most biological effects, provided the dose exceeds a minimum amount, the consequences are proportional to the total accumulated dose of high-energy radiation; while for genetic effects there seems to be no threshold of effectiveness whatsoever. That is to say, even the smallest increments of dose play a proportional part, so that the total accumulated dose is the measure that must be watched. In areas of heavy fallout, shelters should be constructed to provide a hundredfold reduction in the fallout intensity. This should generally suffice to keep the first-day dose below 100 r. The basement shelter which provides a protection factor of 10 or 20 is not adequate for this, although such shelters would of course be sufficient in areas where the fallout during the first day was much less, not exceeding 1000 to 2000 roentgens. If the exposure during the first day can be kept under 100 roentgens, for the first week under 150 roentgens, and for the first months under 200 roentgens acute radiation sickness could probably be prevented, since much of the dose would be accumulated at a relatively low dose rate, which is less effective in producing biological damage than a comparable dose delivered very quickly. For the purposes of the following discussion, however, we must suppose that many, if not a majority of, survivors after a 10,000-megaton attack on the United States would receive a total accumulated dose exceeding 200 roentgens. During the second month the outdoor dose might still exceed 200 r and during the third month 100 r, so that decontamination procedures and indoor living for much of the time would still be required.

In the 1959 hearings it was stated that the postulated 1500-megaton attack would destroy approximately one quarter of all the dwellings in the country, and would damage another 18 per cent of them sufficiently to require evacuation for major repairs. Moreover, about 5 per cent of the undamaged dwellings would have to be evacuated for several months to a year because of heavy fallout contamination. Without making detailed calculations it is evident that a 10,000-megaton attack would destroy or severely damage most of the dwellings except in areas remote from cities and military targets. Those who survive in shelters must therefore expect to live in them for prolonged periods beyond the two to three weeks of acute fallout danger.

From these considerations we can come quickly to some idea of what sorts of shelters would really be effective in the event of any such war. An adequate shelter outside the metropolitan area should be fireproof and provided with proper ventilation and air filtration for the expected number of inmates. It should have its own private water supply, such as a well, and its own sanitary and bathing facilities; food and medicines for a stay of two weeks per person; battery-operated radio and light system; radiation monitoring devices; decontamination equipment; fuel for cooking and heating; and sufficient clothing per person. Not least important are the psychological preventives of boredom and claustrophobia—games, books, magazines—for if the shelters ever need to be used there will be no television programs to watch, and no radio programs to listen to except military and civil defense bulletins. What most people seem not to realize is that there will be no electric current, that conventional sources of light and heat will be unavailable.

Inside the incendiary radius extending outward from each detonation, but outside the blast radius, shelters must have additional features if they are to serve to preserve life. Protection against fallout alone is inadequate here. Even here the shelters must withstand blast pressures up to 5 pounds per square inch. They must be insulated and be tightly sealable and have their own oxygen supply and cooling system sufficient for the duration of fire storms. Food and medicines should be provided for at least one month's needs per person. Perhaps the most important requirement here is that of trained personnel able to monitor the levels of radiation inside and outside the shelter, able to run the machinery needed to supply such a shelter with ventilation and air filtration, oxygen supply and carbon dioxide removal, lighting, heating, and able to give medical services. Under such conditions community shelters and a high degree of organization and training seem indispensable.

The provision of such shelters is not impossible for a nation. Within limits, Sweden has done so already for a portion of its population. To do so is, however, enormously more expensive than is any program currently contemplated by our government. Even a shelter outside the metropolitan areas, such as the one described, and suitable for 4 to 6 persons, will cost upwards of $4000. This statement is made on the basis of the experience of a fallout expert who has actually constructed such a shelter in the Maryland countryside. Yet, it must be emphasized, no simple construction of railroad ties and sandbags can be of much value unless built in a very remote place and unless the powers agree to engage in nuclear war, so to speak, with both hands tied behind their backs. On the other hand, the provision of really adequate shelters of the types described and the necessary regimentation of society needed to implement the program, would not only require an outlay of funds, at a minimum of $1000 per person, of close to three times our annual defense budget, but would—so many persons fear—change the structure of American society irrevocably into that of the closely regimented armed camp, the very image of the totalitarian society we most dislike. An even more immediate threat might be the

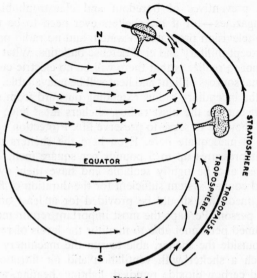

FIGURE 1.

likelihood that the very sight of our nation engaged in taking such measures of defense would convince the opponent that we had determined to make the first, the "pre-emptive," strike and would thus bring upon us the very horror we most hoped to escape.

The Delayed Fallout

The problem of world-wide or "delayed" fallout is distinct from that of the local fallout. It consists of two components, corresponding to the levels of the atmosphere which the fallout particles reach and from which they descend. The lower level of the atmosphere, the level of winds, clouds, rain and snow, is known as the troposphere. Above it is the stratosphere. The boundary between these is called the tropopause (Fig. 1). This boundary is higher in the tropics, where it is found rather constantly at about 55,000 feet, than toward the poles, where it varies between 25,000 and 45,000 feet depending upon the time of day, season, and latitude.

The radioactive particles that enter the troposphere circulate about the earth from west to east, carried by the prevailing winds, until brought down through adherence to raindrops, flakes of snow, or other forms of precipitation. The fallout pattern is often very spotty as a consequence of the irregularities of precipitation. Little of the material produced crosses the equator; it tends to concentrate in the mid-latitudes, between 30° and 60° N if the detonation occurred in the Northern Hemisphere. This zone happens to fall, of course, mainly where human populations are dense.

There is a marked break, or gap, in the tropopause in temperate latitudes, and this break moves north or south with the seasons. Through it passes most of the transfer of air from the stratosphere to the troposphere. As a consequence, radioactive material injected into the stratosphere by a nuclear explosion will come down sooner if it is injected in the far north, since it has but a little way to go to the gap in the tropopause, than when injected near the equator, since then it must circulate gradually to the polar regions before it can reverse direction and reach the gap. It follows that the average residence time of fallout material in the stratosphere is very different in the two cases, being about six months in the case of polar injection and about 2½ years in the case of injection near the equator. The exposure of populations living in the Northern Hemisphere for any given initial amount of fission products is of course much greater in the former case. Very little of the fission products that reach the stratosphere crosses the equator, not more than 5 to 10 per cent of the total.

Tropospheric and stratospheric fallout together represent the world-wide fallout, in contradistinction to the local fallout that occurs in the immediate vicinity of an explosion. In the case of a nuclear war such as we are considering, it is the amount of this delayed fallout that will affect the populations of nontarget nations. Had it not been for the monitoring of the fallout from weapons tests conducted heretofore, we would have no way of estimating this hazard; but as it is, from the exposure to fallout from the 92 megatons of fission products produced by the weapons tests in the period 1952-58, we can extrapolate very simply to the exposures to be expected by neutral nations in the event of a 20,000-megaton war involving the United States, the U.S.S.R., and probably Western Europe. The population of the United States lives in the latitudes between 30° and 60° N, and because many of the tests were held in Nevada and yielded tropospheric fallout on the United States in particular, the exposure of the American population to fallout is about maximum in the world at the present time. It is stated in the new edition of *The Effects of Nuclear Weapons* (1962)[5] to amount to a whole-body dose of 98 millirems, approximately one-tenth of a roentgen. This is one-seventieth of the amount of natural radiation received during 70 years, on the average, by members of our population living at sea-level; or about one per cent of the natural radiation received in 70 years at high altitudes, such as that of Denver. If half of the 20,000 megatons result from fission, the delayed fallout to be expected would be close to 100 times as great as that from the weapons tests during the 1952-58 period. In short, it would amount to about 10 roentgens. Of course, there is some error of measurement in the amount of fallout to which the American population has been exposed to date. The radiation dose might be greater, perhaps even 0.2 r. Against any such increase of the estimate, however, we must offset several things. First, the nontarget nations may well lie south of latitude 30° N and consequently would receive a lesser amount of fallout. Second, since much of the tropospheric fallout will descend on the countries where the explosions occur, or to the east of them, the larger part of the tropospheric fallout from a nuclear war such as that postulated would spare the Philippines, southern China, Siam and Burma, India, and Mexico, Central America, Colombia, and Venezuela. And south of the equator less than half as much fallout would be expected.

What, then, would a general dose of 10 r north of the equator, or one of 5 r south of the equator, do to the local populations? As we shall see, some radiation damage is to be expected. But many of us have received larger doses of high-energy radiation in a hospital or physician's office, from fluoroscopy or half a dozen radiographs, and no one is *visibly* the worse for it. One may, I think, conclude that even a much larger nuclear war than the one I have taken as a basis of discussion would not wipe out human life or destroy civilization, even in the Northern Hemisphere. In fact, it seems reasonable to say that the surest way to turn over the world to Communism would be for the great nuclear powers of today to destroy each other, and thus leave the future to Red China.

The specific biological effects of fallout are to be gauged in terms of these ranges of whole-body dose we have found to be applicable: doses over 1000 r, death virtually certain; doses around 450 r, death of 50%, recovery of 50% (LD_{50}); 200 to 300 r, severe radiation sickness; 100 to 200 r, mild radiation sickness; below 100 r, no evident immediate effects. The effects of the radiation are plainly most severe upon tissues composed of proliferating cells. When cells are dividing, the hereditary material of the nucleus of each cell condenses; the chromosomes make their appearance, first as long slender threads, each one double as a result of previous replication. The chromosomes thicken, coil up, become covered with some insulating material, and the duplicate members of each original chromosome separate and pass to opposite ends of a spindle, so that they find their way, one of each kind, into the daughter cells. It is in the early stages of this mitosis, as it is called, that the chromosomes are specially liable to fracture and damage by radiation. It has now been clearly demonstrated that most killing of cells by radiation, particularly at doses under 1000 r, is through damage to the chromosomes, and not to any other parts of the cells.[6] These facts explain why it is *dividing* cells that are killed, and consequently why the primary injuries done by radiation are to the skin, the lining of the digestive tract, the bone marrow, the kidneys, and the reproductive cells. All of these tissues or organs consist of more or less rapidly dividing cells that must frequently replace cells that die. On the other hand, nervous tissue, which is almost totally nondividing after fetal life, is far more resistant to high-energy radiation.

Somatic Effects of Atomic Radiations

The effects of radiation on the human body are often divided into somatic effects and genetic effects. These are not really different in the ultimate character of what the radiation does to the components of the cells. The difference is simply that in the case of damage done to reproductive cells, housed in the ovaries or testes (the gonads), any damage done to the chromosomes and genes may be passed on to some future descendant; whereas in the case of damage done in the somatic cells which constitute all the rest of the body, damage done is not passed on to another generation, but is eliminated with the death of the cell or person receiving the radiation.

Severe radiation sickness begins with nausea and vomiting. Diarrhea and loss of appetite follow. These are symptoms of the killing of innumerable cells lining the digestive tract. Later come hemorrhages, from a loss of blood platelets needed for blood clotting, and a startling drop in the number of white blood cells. Along with these effects there is, naturally, a lowered resistance of the body to bacterial infections and a depression in the formation of antibodies, since the bone marrow and lymphoid tissues are being depleted. The hair falls out. Unless such measures are taken as the complete replacement of the bone marrow by implantation from a normal donor, death in severe cases follows after steplike rises in temperature. In the severest cases, death is a consequence of direct degeneration of the tissues following killing of too many of the cells. In less severe cases, death often comes from infections against which the body has little or no remaining resistance.

Mild radiation sickness is similar except in severity. After the first symptoms develop, they may pass and a period of days or even weeks may elapse before there is a recurrence following the first appearance of the blood changes. Antibiotics, to resist the infections that may develop, are effective in these milder cases.

There are several kinds of long-term, or delayed, somatic effects. One of these is the induction of malignancies which may appear after a latent period of several years. In addition to cancers of lung, stomach, breast, skin, ovary, and other exposed organs, leukemia, which may be described as a neoplasm of the white blood cells, may be produced. Thyroid carcinoma may result from iodine-131; bone cancer may follow the concentration of strontium-90 in the bones. All these sorts of malignancies occur in the population ordinarily, so that what is observed is never more than a statistical increase, often very small and difficult to discern or to establish as significant.

Cataracts, resulting in blindness, may arise from opacity of the lens of the eye induced either by neutrons or gamma rays in the direct radiation. The flux of such radiation in delayed fallout is probably much too low to produce cataracts. One would judge from the occurrence in the survivors of the Hiroshima and Nagasaki explosions that cataracts follow only from a sufficiently great exposure (300 r or more) to the initial nuclear radiation. X-rays, of course, will act similarly, and the exposure of the eyes to large doses 'must be carefully avoided.

A less obvious somatic effect of radiation is shortening of the normal life span. Children exposed to high-energy radiation may exhibit a slower rate of development and delay in attaining maturity, even when no obvious defects are apparent; but more startling is the fact that irradiated children or adults never live as long as comparable groups of unirradiated persons. This is best shown in the results of some of the experiments done with mice and rats.

If animals are irradiated with, say, a 300 r whole-body dose and are then permitted to recover, or if they are given even a dose insufficient to cause obvious radiation sickness, and if they are then later subjected to a killing dose of high-energy radiation and compared with a group never previously irradiated, it is characteristically found that it takes a considerably smaller dose to kill all the previously irradiated animals (or to kill half, the LD_{50}) than to kill the previously unirradiated ones. One might say that the reserves which the body possesses as a defense against the effects of radiation and upon which recuperation depends have been depleted. Moreover, this depletion is strictly proportional to the amount of radiation previously received; that is to say, the shortening of life is directly proportional to the total accumulated dose. The most careful and extensive experiments of this kind, to my knowledge, have been performed recently by Patricia Lindop and J. Rotblat in England.[7] Using mice all of a particular age and belonging to a homogeneous genetic strain, they compared groups unirradiated and irradiated with doses of x-rays ranging from 50 to 780 roentgens. The mice were followed through life until all had died, and each one was then autopsied to determine the cause of its death. The shortening of life produced by the radiation was found to be directly and linearly proportional to the size of the administered dose. There was not the slightest indication that the smallest dose administered produced less than the expected amount of effect; in other words, there was no indication of any threshold below which the radiation fails to shorten life, even though the 50 r dose is well below the level which produces any visible symptoms. Moreover— a point to be emphasized—the deaths which occurred were from the usual causes characteristic of this strain of mice, and not from any unusual causes attributable to the radiation. It is as if the radiation had merely advanced the time of death from the usual causes, as if it had removed a segment of the life-span at the time when the irradiation was administered and left the irradiated animals biologically older than their chronological age would indicate!

The life-shortening found in the mouse study was 5.66 weeks per 100 r, or half a day per roentgen. The LD_{50} for these mice (700 r) would diminish the life-span by 38 per cent. Since the LD_{50} for human beings is thought to be closer to 450 r than to 700 r, we probably experience a greater life-shortening effect for a given exposure than a mouse does. But then the human life span is also longer—in fact, about 26 times as long. Though the ex-trapolation is none too secure, we might multiply the half day per roentgen by the factor expressing the difference in the life spans of the two species, on the assumption that the mouse simply uses up its biological potential at a faster rate than a human. In that case, 1 roentgen of whole-body irradiation would be expected to re-duce the human life span by 13 days. If we use the LD_{50} values to obtain the proportional sensitivity of mouse and man, the short-ening of the human life span by 1 roentgen would be expected to be even greater, amounting to 3.2 weeks.

It must be pointed out that the life-shortening found by Lindop and Rotblat in irradiated mice exceeds that found by other inves-tigators. This is probably because Lindop and Rotblat used mice at the most radiation-sensitive age of life. This procedure would be comparable to studying the effects on humans of irradiation during early childhood. Adults would prove to be considerably less affected. Yet rough as the extrapolation is, it provides our only yardstick for deducing the life-shortening effects of radiation and fallout in the event of nuclear war. Survivors in the combatant na-tions will very likely receive 200 to 300 r of whole-body radiation, and this amount might shorten their lives as much as 8 years if they were children, less if they were adult, even if they escaped ra-diation sickness altogether. As for the inhabitants of noncom-batant nations, the 5 r to 10 r they might receive would also be ex-pected to produce some degree of life-shortening, but by so few days that in countries where most people do not attain the full nat-ural life-span anyway it would not be noticeable. It must be added, however, that the doses used in these mouse experiments were "acute" doses, that is, were administered rapidly. We do not know at the present time whether the slower administration of the same total dose, as from fallout, would produce so severe an ef-fect. There is some reason to suppose that it might not, for a low dose rate yields a lower genetic effect, as will be seen.

Finally, among the somatic effects of high-energy radiations, we must consider induced sterility, for this is a common consequence when sizeable doses of radiation are administered to the gonads. In the case of the mouse, the male immediately becomes sterile, owing to the killing of the mature and near-mature germ cells; fertility gradually returns, as the more resistant spermatogonia de-velop and mature into spermatozoa. In the case of the female mouse, the opposite pattern occurs. She remains fertile for a time, since the relatively mature oocytes are fairly resistant to high doses of radiation. Then she becomes totally and permanently sterile. Even 50 r will produce this permanent sterility if administered at a high dose rate, or 80 r administered at a low dose rate. If women in this respect responded to radiation like female mice, the most horrifying effect of nuclear war would be the prevention of further reproduction, especially since the younger females in the population would experience total sterility throughout life. Fortunately, the mouse appears to be an exception among mammals, even among rodents, in this respect. Female guinea pigs and hamsters, as well as monkeys, are much more resistant than female mice to the sterilizing effects of radiation. It seems that in the female mice the oocytes in the ovary go into a prolonged arrest in development at a more sensitive stage in their maturation process than is the case in the female guinea pig. This difference holds true for the other species mentioned, and probably also for the female dog and human female, for which there is evidence that sterility is produced only by much higher doses (several hundred roentgens). It is consequently very unlikely that the women and female children of noncombatant countries, even in the Northern Hemisphere, would exhibit any detectable loss of fertility in the aftermath of a nuclear war of the dimensions I have assumed; but still a word of caution needs to be added respecting the survivors in the combatant countries themselves. If these have received an accumulated dose of 200 r or more, even though most of it might be in the post-shelter period at relatively low dose rates, a major effect upon the surviving population might still be from the sterilizing effects of radiation. The males would tend to be sterile during the immediate period after exposure, and by the time they were recovering fertility, the adult females would lose their fertility. The younger females might never become fertile. We need much more information about these matters than now exists. Is the reduction of fertility, like the shortening of the life span, proportional to the total dose? In experiments with the fruitfly Drosophila, I have found that even a dose of 5 r produces a decline of fertility of about 1 per cent. This would be of no consequence to a species like the human one, which has a far greater potential fecundity than is needed to keep the birth rate at or above the level of the death rate. In the aftermath of nuclear war, however, piled on innumerable other difficulties and woes, the diminished reproduction of the population is not to be ignored.

The Genetic Effects of Atomic Radiations

Three main types of genetic effects produced by ionizing radiation may be distinguished: chromosome breaks, chromosome nondisjunction leading to extra or to missing chromosomes, and transmissible mutations unassociated with obvious changes of the first two sorts. In previous discussions of the biological effects of radiation, even in the updated 1960 Report of the Genetics Committee of the National Academy of Sciences[8] on this subject, nothing was said about the second of these categories, for it was only in 1959 that evidence was discovered that nondisjunction produces abnormal chromosome numbers in human beings.

Chromosomes each possess one, and normally only one, structure that during cell division attaches it to the spindle and serves as a locomotor organ ensuring that it will move to one pole of the spindle or the other, and thus become properly included in the nucleus of one daughter cell or the other. When a chromosome reproduces itself, this structure (the centromere or kinetochore) also splits or reproduces, so that each daughter chromosome has a centromere at the same location in the string of genes composing the chromosome. When a chromosome or chromatid (a daughter chromosome not yet separated from its sister-chromatid) is fractured by radiation, the piece thus separated from connection with its centromere forms a fragment that cannot move appropriately as the normal chromosomes do. The fragment may drift out into the cytoplasm, in which case it is attacked by enzymes that destroy it, and all its genes will then be lost from the daughter cell that otherwise would have received them. Unless the fragment is very small, this consequence is nearly always fatal to the cell. Geneticists say the effect is that of a *dominant lethal*. The second thing that may happen, in case more than one chromosome or chromatid is fractured, is that two broken ends may adhere, for they behave as if they were sticky. In that case, if both fragments adhere they will fail to possess a centromere and be lost, as before; while the adhesion of two pieces each of which possesses a centromere will produce a chromosome bridge when the two centromeres go in opposite directions. The tug of war that results commonly ends either in the loss of the abnormal chromosome in the cytoplasm of the cell, or in rupture of the bridge, which is followed by further losses of bits of chromosome or by further adhesions. Only when broken ends adhere in such a way that every piece of chromosome possesses one, and only one, centromere will a transmissible and heritable effect occur. At low and intermediate doses of radiation there are rarely two independent breaks in the same nucleus. Consequently chromosome breakage at low and intermediate doses, below 1000 r, results chiefly in losses of pieces of chromosome, in deficiencies of usually many genes, and in death of the affected cells.

Single chromosome breaks have been shown repeatedly, in published experiments done by J. G. Carlson,[9] M. A. Bender,[10] N. P. Dubinin and collaborators,[11] to increase linearly with the administered dose of high-energy radiation. These experiments have been carried out with human cells of a variety of types, growing in artificial cultures outside the body, as well as in white blood cells irradiated just as they were drawn from the body. Especially clear results have been obtained in still unpublished experiments done in my own laboratory by a student, J. G. Brewen, who has used the corneal epithelium of the Chinese hamster, irradiated with x-rays in its normal position in the eye. These experiments, like those of Bender and Dubinin et al., indicate that the frequency of chromosome breakage is linearly proportional to the dose in roentgens, at relatively low doses. Brewen's data cover the range from 10 r to 150 r very adequately. They show an average frequency of breakage of 0.0035 per cell per roentgen; Bender's results on the white blood cells yield a frequency of 0.0024 per cell per roentgen. For tissues comparable to these, a dose of 300 to 400 r will produce one chromosome break, usually cell-lethal, in every cell. It is easy to see why doses in this range are so drastic in effect. The miracle is that any individual so exposed can survive!

Because the production of a chromosome break is usually lethal to the cell, or to one of the two daughter cells, such effects are not likely to be passed on to the next generation. The principal results will be to add to the sterility burden produced by other effects of the radiation. Clearly, since reproductive cells are cells that must divide, except for those already mature, which are likewise quite sensitive to radiation, a dose of 300 to 400 r would seem likely to produce a grave loss of fertility. Even a dose of 10 r might be expected to reduce fertility proportionately, perhaps by 2 to 4 per cent. Experiments done with the fruitfly Drosophila in my own laboratory confirm this prediction. The fertility of unirradiated males and females was compared with that of males and females exposed to a dose of 5 r each. In a total of 1,360,948 progeny, there was a 1 per cent reduction in the number of offspring produced by the irradiated parents.

The second type of genetic damage which may be produced by radiation is a consequence of errors which result in an extra chromosome of some sort, or one chromosome too few, in the fertilized egg or in one of the cells arising from it early in the course of development. In 1959 it was discovered, almost simultaneously in France and in Great Britain, that most cases of "Mongoloid" idiocy are attributable to the presence of an extra chromosome, named number 21 from its relative rank in size among the 23 chromosomes of the egg or sperm. Shortly afterwards, two forms of sexual maldevelopment accompanied by sterility were discovered to arise, the one from the presence of an extra sex chromosome, the other from the lack of a sex chromosome normally present. Ever since 1913 abnormalities of this same kind had been known in fruitflies, and later they were found (in 1922) to be increased in frequency after the parent flies were exposed to x-rays. Similar abnormalities have more recently been found in mice.

These errors of chromosome number, which may be classed as a sort of mutation, arise in two general ways. The commonest is probably through what is called nondisjunction, that is, a failure of the maternal and paternal chromosomes of the same kind, following their close pairing in the maturation of the germ-cells, to separate from each other and go singly into the reproductive cells. The result would be formation of one reproductive cell with an extra chromosome and another cell with one chromosome too few. The other way in which such errors arise is through the loss of a chromosome from the nucleus of the fertilized egg. Recent studies at the Oak Ridge National Laboratory by Liane B. Russell and C. L. Saylors show that when mouse spermatozoa are irradiated, either before or after the transfer to the female during mating, loss of a chromosome is not uncommon. In fact, the frequency of loss of one of the paternal chromosomes is considerably greater when the irradiation hits the paternal nucleus after the sperm has already penetrated the egg during the fertilization process than when the sperm is x-rayed in the male parent prior to mating. In the former case, 5.2 per cent of cases of loss of the sex chromosome occurred from a dose of 100 r, in the latter case only 0.2 per cent.[12]

Losses of chromosomes other than the sex chromosomes are fatal in early development in the mouse, and presumably in human beings losses of most chromosomes except the sex chromosomes and the smaller chromosomes (21 and 22) are likewise fatal. Many particular kinds of loss have now been identified and are known to cause multiple congenital defects resulting in neonatal death. In any event, all previous estimates of the frequency of detrimental mutations produced by ionizing radiations must now be increased by some, still uncertain, amount to allow for this novel and unsuspected type of human damage. At the present time one cannot say how many Mongoloid idiots and sexually aberrant persons, as well as fetal and neonatal deaths, have been produced by radiation. It may indeed be a small proportion of the total. Yet there is no reason to doubt that radiation will cause such defects, particularly if administered to the female parent or the just-fertilized egg. The continuous radiation from the surroundings after a large-scale nuclear attack might produce a notable increase of this sort of mutational defect, even though in lands where the radiation from delayed fallout was 10 r or less no difference from previous conditions in this respect would be apparent.

Transmissible mutations induced by high-energy radiations include both small deficiencies, usually at the lower limit of detection even in the giant salivary gland chromosomes of the fruitfly, and also what the geneticist calls "point mutations," cases where the lesion or alteration in the chromosome is below the resolution of current microscopy. Both of these types of mutation are related to the dosage of radiation in the same way. They increase in direct linear proportionality to the dose. That is to say, double the dose and you obtain twice as many mutations; triple the dose, and you obtain three times as many; and so on. Much effort has gone into the establishment of this relationship for relatively low doses of radiation, since the dosage curve, when extrapolated downward from the experimentally established levels to lower doses, always appeared to hit as its origin (at zero dose) the level of the established spontaneous mutation rate. In other words, there was no evidence of any threshold below which the radiation was ineffective in producing mutations. On the contrary, one would conclude that every increment of radiation, however small, produced its proportional effect upon the mutation rate.

Most of the early studies were limited to treatment of the male, and usually to treatment of mature spermatozoa. Later it became clear that such results do not give a sufficient picture of the effects of radiation upon a population, because they neglect the different responses of the mature females and particularly of the immature germ cells (which might be carried either in immature individuals or in mature individuals). The great studies of the Manhattan Project were, in fact, carried out principally with male fruitflies. Super-teams of geneticists and technical assistants succeeded in showing, first, that 50 roentgens, and later, 25 roentgens, produce exactly the frequencies of mutations expected in proportion to those obtained at higher doses.[13] Notwithstanding, as concern grew about the accumulated effects of fallout or of the doses given for medical and dental diagnosis and treatment, there were doubters who wondered if 10 r, or 5 r, or 3 r, would still produce the expected number of mutations, or even any at all. For this reason, my colleagues and I have carried out, over a period of three years, what we sometimes call our "megafly experiment," since we have examined considerably more than a million flies for mutations induced by a dose of 5 roentgens given to each of the parents. The experiment was repeated fifty times, each time with exactly matched irradiated and unirradiated cultures, coded to prevent any possible bias on the part of the scorers had they known which series had been irradiated. A dominant type of transmissible mutation occurring at more than fifty loci in the chromosomes was the basis of the test. These minute bristle mutations are either point mutations or small deficiencies, and earlier tests had shown that, for a given dose of x-rays, they arise with equal frequency in the spermatozoa and mature oocytes. The results show definitely that even the 5 r dose produces mutations at the proportion expected on the basis of a linear dosage curve, that is, 5 per cent as many as a dose or 100 r, or 0.5 per cent as many as a dose of 100 r.[14]

Together with the evidence from the production of chromosome breaks by low doses in individual cells and tissues, this evidence reinforces what was put in carefully chosen words by the Genetics Committee of the National Academy of Sciences Committee on the Biological Effects of Radiation, in 1956: "*Any* radiation is genetically undesirable, since any radiation induces harmful mutations. . . . The genetic harm is proportional to the total dose." [15] And, in the 1958 Report of the United Nations Scientific Committee on the Effects of Atomic Radiation: "Even the smallest amounts of radiation are liable to cause deleterious genetic, and perhaps also somatic, effects." [16]

The most unexpected and most discussed development during recent years in the study of radiation-induced mutations has emerged from the mouse experiments conducted by W. L. Russell and his colleagues at the Oak Ridge National Laboratory.[17] These experiments were done by irradiating mice lacking any known mutations and then mating them to a strain which carries seven different recessive point-mutations. The offspring of such a cross would be heterozygous, that is, would carry at each of the 7 loci a normal and a recessive allele. They would therefore be non-mutant in appearance unless a mutation—either a point-mutation or a deficiency—had been induced by the radiation at one of the seven loci. The earlier experiments were performed by treating the male with x-rays, waiting until it had fully recovered its fertility, and then mating it to the tester type of female. The results, over a range of doses from 300 r to 1000 r, showed the expected increase in frequency of mutations to be linearly proportional to the increase in dose. The later experiments compared the results just described with those obtained when a gamma-ray emitter such as cobalt-60 or cesium-137 was used instead of x-rays, and the rate at which the dose was delivered was greatly reduced. The earlier dose rate was 90 r per minute and the new one was 0.009 r per minute, that is, ten thousand times as slow. The total doses administered were of course adjusted to be the same. To everyone's surprise, since previous experiments in producing mutations at different dose rates had shown no differences between the effects of high dose rates and low dose rates whenever the total dose was the same, there now appeared to be a considerable difference. At the low dose rate only about one-fourth as many mutations were produced as at the high dose rate, for each and any total dose. The reason why the effect had never been found before is now reasonably clear. The earlier experiments, which were performed largely with fruitflies, had involved only the treatment of mature spermatozoa, whereas by Russell's method the treated cells which functioned in fertilization were immature germ-cells (spermatogonia) at the time of their treatment. Spermatozoa, although very sensitive to ionizing radiation, are nondividing cells; but spermatogonia are dividing cells, and the conditions prevailing in them evidently allow some sort of repair or restoration to occur in the case of many mutations which in spermatozoa are unable to undergo repair.

The most recent studies by Russell's group indicate that the effect of the dose rate also exists in the maturation of the female reproductive cells, or oocytes, and may in fact be greater in magnitude in them than in the male. For both sexes together, about six times as many mutations are induced at a high dose rate as at a low dose rate. The implications of these findings for the interpretation of genetic damage from fallout are obvious. In the event of a nuclear war, much of the exposure of the survivors in a target country will occur at fairly high dose rates, from the local fallout within the first two days after the nuclear explosions. Perhaps half of the exposure, however, would come from delayed fallout, and in this case the dose rate will be relatively low. On the other hand, exposed populations in noncombatant countries will be exposed entirely to delayed fallout, that is, to radiation at a low dose rate. If the human reproductive cells respond to radiation like those of the mouse, mutations will be considerably less frequent under these circumstances.

Russell has also recently tested several intermediate levels of dose rate. In the experiments in which males are treated, a dose rate of 9 r per minute is intermediate in its genetic effect, while a dose of 0.8 r per minute is already at the minimal effectiveness of the dose rate a hundred times as slow. When females are treated, the situation turns out somewhat differently. The minimum level is not reached until a dose rate below 0.8 r per minute is utilized.[18]

Several important conclusions may already be drawn, although confirmation of these results, particularly for other species of animals, is still needed. One point of emphasis is that the male and the female reproductive cells cannot be expected to behave toward radiation exactly alike. The situation is complex. Secondly, one should emphasize that in terms of human exposure 0.8 r per minute is not what would be considered a very low dose rate, since at that rate it would require only 12 to 13 minutes to reach the level of exposure which is the accepted maximum permissible limit for gonadal exposure of the population to man-made radiation. Thirdly, there is no ground, on the basis of Russell's data, for concluding either that the relation of mutation frequency to dose is not one of linear proportionality or for concluding that there is any threshold at very low doses. In both of these important respects, the data show precisely the contrary. For the low dose rates, the frequency of mutations still increases linearly with the dose. A total dose of only 86 r at the low dose rate produced exactly the frequency of mutations expected on the basis of the frequencies of mutations produced at doses of 300 r, 516 r, and 861 r also administered at the low dose rate. There is no indication of a threshold.

Several recent discoveries tend to offset the lowering of the estimated genetic damage because of the dose rate findings. Especially important is the induction of mutations by carbon-14, which is produced in the fusion process, has a long half-life of over 5000 years, and is readily incorporated into the genetic material of the very genes and chromosomes themselves. Recent estimates by geneticists are given in the Report of the Federal Radiation Council (1962) entitled *Health Implications of Fallout from Nuclear Weapons Testing through 1961*.[19] Whereas in the first generation of children of persons exposed the number of gross physical or mental defects arising from mutations produced by carbon-14 is estimated to be only one-tenth of the number produced by the fallout, the total number through all future generations is estimated to be twice as great as the number arising from the delayed fallout. Local fallout from nearby explosions is of course not meant here, since the estimates were based on the effects of fallout produced by weapons testing to date. Since the survivors in an attacked country would probably receive a large part of their exposure from delayed fallout, the effects of carbon-14 will by no means be negligible.

What would a dose of 200 roentgens received by every survivor in an attacked country produce, in genetic terms? From James V. Neel's estimates presented in the 1959 hearings we can get some idea.[20] If we assume a constant size of population, forty million survivors might produce in the succeeding 30 generations some 1,200 million descendants. Among these, to go by Neel's minimum estimates, there would be about 10 million deaths occurring at or before birth from genetic defects, about half a million living defectives, and about 25 million persons with impaired vigor or fertility. In Western Europe and the U.S.S.R. there might be in the aggregate four times as many. In the descendants of the 2 billion persons living in noncombatant parts of the Northern Hemisphere, the estimated 10 roentgens they might receive on the average would yield 25 million deaths at or before birth, one and a quarter million living defective persons, and 62.5 million individuals with impaired vigor or fertility. Because of the enormous difference in the sizes of the surviving populations, the small dose from delayed fallout would in the long run produce almost as many genetic disabilities and deaths in the noncombatant peoples of the world as in the survivors of the nuclear combat.

The estimate may be made in another way. The number of genetically defective persons born alive probably amounts to 4 per cent of all births. This estimate, somewhat higher than the one used in the National Academy of Sciences Genetics Committee's Report of 1956, is based on the tabulation of specific hereditary traits and their estimated incidences given in the Report of the United Nations Scientific Committee on the Effects of Atomic Radiation, Annex H, in 1958. By genetic defects we mean, of course, not gross monsters in the majority of cases, but the more common kind of biochemical defects, the so-called "inborn errors of metabolism," which are now present in the population and some of which are familiar to any of us. They would include, for example, defects of the gastrointestinal tract, such as intestinal polyps; of the blood, such as hemophilia; of immunity mechanisms, such as agammaglobulinemia; of kidney function, such as cystinuria; nervous and mental disorders, such as epilepsy and schizophrenia; muscular and skeletal defects, such as muscular dystrophy; endocrine disorders, such as pituitary dwarfness or diabetes; reproductive effects, producing sterility; and a long list of others, from albinism and achondroplastic dwarfness through deafness, gout, and myopia, to xeroderma pigmentosum and xanthoma tuberosum.

By a recognized genetic principle, a doubling of the mutation rate will in time lead to a doubling of the amount of evident genetic defect in the population. The question, then, is how much high-energy radiation will double the previous (spontaneous) mutation rate which is responsible for the genetic defects currently present in the population. For a variety of organisms, including some plants, the fruitfly Drosophila, and the mouse, doubling doses for transmissible mutations of the point mutation or small deficiency types have been determined. There is astonishing uniformity in the range of this so-called "doubling dose," which generally falls within the range of 30 to 80 roentgens, with 40 to 60 r more common. In my own megafly experiment, described previously, the doubling dose turned out to be 60 r. For chromosome breaks it is of course much less, but we are concerned with nontransmissible types of mutation here. One cannot assert positively that such a value applies to human beings, but there is no reason to suppose that it does not. One would therefore conclude that a 10 r dose to an entire population might produce one-fourth to one-sixth of the number of harmful mutations occurring spontaneously in every generation. A dose of 200 r, on the other hand, would produce 3 to 5 times as many as normally arise spontaneously.

The number of genetically defective individuals would consequently rise in the populations exposed to delayed fallout to approach a new level of 5 per cent, or somewhat less. In the surviving populations of the target countries, on the other hand, the expected final level would rise to 12 to 20 per cent of births. True, this would not occur until many generations had passed, and if the exposure were limited to a single generation the level would gradually drop back again to the original level.

Could a population withstand the social effects of such a high level of genetic defect? It probably could, although in the harsh conditions of life that would very likely prevail in the devastated parts of the world after a nuclear war, it is scarcely conceivable that our present tender regard for the preservation of life could continue to be manifested toward the handicapped, deformed, and weakly individuals who would constitute so tremendous a social burden. In the bitter struggle for the necessities of life, what is likely to become of the ethics of modern man? One of the gravest losses which society may experience might be, under these conditions, a reversion to the ethics of the ape man.

A question often asked is the following: "Aren't some mutations beneficial? Can't an increase in the number of mutations be expected to produce some increase in human evolution, some improvement in the over-all capacities of mankind?" The question reveals a grave misunderstanding. Some mutations are indeed beneficial, and some that are detrimental in certain environments may be less so, or may even be beneficial, in other circumstances. Evolution is based on the occurrence of such mutations. But it is equally important to understand that the great majority of mutations produce defects and do harm, if for no other reason than because natural selection over countless generations has already been at work selecting and grouping into harmonious genotypes those mutations of which human genes are capable. To the extent that we are well adapted to our present environment, genetic changes are likely to produce a lower fitness. Such effects of mutation as have been analyzed biochemically show that the usual consequence of mutation is to alter the structure of some enzyme or to cease producing it. In either case, the efficiency of some particular step in the body's metabolism is impaired, or blocked altogether. Genes control the nature of our enzymes, the enzymes needed in growth, development, and maintenance, and we do not possess very many, if any, superfluous enzymes. Geneticists are therefore not surprised to find, in actual experiments, that the overwhelming majority of mutations are damaging. The proportion of harmful mutations may run as high as 95 to 99 per cent of all mutations, according to some estimates. A general increase in the frequency of mutation therefore multiplies injury far more rapidly than benefit. Only selection can turn the tables, and for it to do so requires generations of the elimination of the "unfit," that is, the less viable, the less reproductive individuals. To gain one beneficial gene, a population has to suffer many "genetic deaths," or eliminations of damaging genes. The choice, therefore, is reduced to this: how high a price in suffering do we want to pay for possible evolutionary gains? It is likely that in large populations the beneficial mutations of nearly every possible sort already exist, though perhaps not in ideal combinations. No one, for the sake of one advantageous trait, would want to be handicapped with twenty defects. We can do considerably better by keeping the mutation rate low, even if long-range improvement of the species is thereby postponed.

The damage done to a population is nevertheless not simply a question of the frequency of the detrimental mutant genes. It also depends on the relative amounts of harm they do to individuals and to society. The 1960 Report of the Genetics Committee of the National Academy of Sciences asks provocatively: "How . . . does one measure quantitatively the relative importance of a stillbirth, a feebleminded child, and a death during adolescence?" [21] Or, one might add, of a death very soon after conception, when the mother is often quite unaware that an abortion has occurred? A tentative beginning of this kind of appraisal has been made by Sewall Wright in an addendum to the Report just mentioned. Much thinking and much investigation must go into this kind of combined genetic and social analysis, however, before appropriate measures of any kind can be recommended.

The Aftermath

One cannot examine the consequences of nuclear war in general biological terms and rest satisfied with an estimate of the immediate effects upon the human population. Man lives in a well-balanced environment, and the profound effects of a nuclear war upon the unsheltered and unshielded organisms that make up his ecological community dare not be forgotten. However adequate our shelters for people, there must remain outside them the animals we have domesticated, the plants we cultivate, the forests and the meadows, the soil, the birds, the insects, and the bacteria—to mention only a part of our community.

The outside levels of radiation, in the event of a 10,000-megaton attack on the United States, will obviously far exceed lethal limits for birds and mammals. Barring special measures for their protection, survivors will find no horses, cattle, pigs, chickens, or other animal sources of food remaining. Without the birds, the insects will take over. Since adult insects are in general very resistant to high-energy radiation, they will remain in large numbers wherever fire has not completely destroyed life. A cockroach, for example, can tolerate 400,000 r and many insects will tolerate 40,000 r or more. The larval forms are more sensitive and might be killed were it not that many of them live and grow under water or under the bark of trees or in similar sheltered places. And if all the larvae perished but the adults were not rendered completely sterile, the populations would soon be replenished. Sterility, in insects, is not produced by doses of less than several thousand roentgens, which is far more than a mammal or bird can tolerate and live, and more than many insects in the continental area are likely to receive as a dose. The insects, unchecked in their ravages, may quickly destroy every green thing left by fire and blast.

The incendiary effects of nuclear weapons are increased by exploding them at high altitudes. According to one estimate, one 10-megaton bomb could spread searing heat over 5000 square miles, which is about the area of the state of Connecticut. The fire storms and lesser fires would hit countryside as well as cities, and depending upon the season of the year and the dryness of the vegetation, might burn off the land over vast stretches. What the fires left, the local fallout would probably kill, since a pine tree can stand only about 500 roentgens, and hardwood trees less than 1000 r. Not only would they be destroyed, but unless somewhere seeds were preserved they could not be replanted. The erosion that would follow, on the unprotected soil, would be frightful to think of. It would probably carry off most of the fallout particles, so that the long-term accumulation of strontium-90 and cesium-

137 in the bodies of the survivors might be far less than one would estimate from an initial contamination running up to 100,000 millicuries per square mile in some areas. But the floods and the loss of the topsoil from most of the continent would be a severe price to pay for nature's clean-up of the radioactive contamination.

Finally, one must think of the bacteria. There are so many bacteria that even at high doses of ionizing radiation some escape its killing effects. Unless the fires did a very thorough clean-up job the millions of unburied corpses of human beings and animals would provide a hotbed for the growth of the organisms of death and decay. Can we believe that in the absence of organized medical services, in the wake of physical and psychic stress, radiation injuries, the destruction of sanitary facilities, and malnutrition, disease would not become rampant? Little serious thought has been given to the prevention of the epidemics that might sweep the land. I have heard it seriously suggested that it would be better, in case of a heavy nuclear attack, if survivors were relatively few and scattered, since in that case there might be a better chance to escape from epidemics, to feed the survivors, and to rebuild a society, than if too many persons were left alive and needing care.

The disorganization of society, the destruction of the laboratories and libraries of science, the obliteration of organized education, the loss of art, music, books, and entertainment must be added to the problems raised by the wreckage of transportation and communication, and the loss of natural resources. Life will be very primitive for the survivors for a long time to come. If America survived at all, could it be as more than a tenth-rate power? Would the more fortunate lands take pity on the country that first produced and used the atom bomb, and later engaged in the accelerating arms race? Does the preservation of the American people and their society, like that of the U.S.S.R. and Western Europe, not demand continued efforts to attain the general and complete nuclear disarmament of all nations?

References

1. Everett, Hugh, III, and Pugh, G. E. The distribution and effects of fallout in large nuclear-weapon campaigns. *Operations Research* 7, 1959. Reprinted in United States Congress, Joint Committee on Atomic Energy. *Biological and Environmental Effects of Nuclear War: Summary analysis of hearings, June 22-26, 1959.* 58 pp. Washington, D. C.: Government Printing Office, 1959. Pp. 859-881.

2. Quoted from *Fallout* (John M. Fowler, ed.), p. 184. Basic Books, New York, 1960.
3. Piel, Gerard. The illusion of civil defense. See p. 57 in this book.
4. Lapp, R. E. Nuclear war, in *Fallout* (John M. Fowler, ed.), pp. 153-173. Basic Books, New York, 1960.
5. *The Effects of Nuclear Weapons* (S. Glasstone, ed.), Revised Edition. U. S. Govt. Printing Office, Washington, 1962. Much of the preceding information is drawn from this manual.
6. Puck, T. T. Action of radiation on mammalian cells. III. Relationship between reproductive death and induction of chromosome anomalies by X-irradiation of euploid human cells in vitro. *Proc. Natl. Acad. Sci. U.S.* 44:772-780, 1958.
7. P. T. Lindop and J. Rotblat. Shortening of life and causes of death in mice exposed to a single whole body dose of radiation, *Nature, 189*: 645-648 (1961).
8. *The Biological Effects of Atomic Radiation, Summary Reports.* National Academy of Sciences—National Research Council, Washington, 1960.
9. J. G. Carlson. An analysis of X-ray induced single breaks in neuroblast chromosomes of the grasshopper (*Chortophaga viridifasciata*). *Proc. Nat. Acad. Sci. U.S.* 27:42-47 (1941).
10. M. A. Bender. X-ray induced chromosome aberrations in mammalian cells *in vivo* and *in vitro*. In *Immediate and Low Level Effects of Ionizing Radiation, Intern. J. Radiation Biol.,* Suppl., 103-118 (1959).
11. N. P. Dubinin, Y. Y. Kerkis, and L. I. Lebedeva. Experimental analysis of the effect of radiation on cellular nuclei in the culture of embryonal human tissues. Soviet Physics Doklady 6:538-540 (1961).
12. Liane B. Russell and C. L. Saylors. Induction of paternal sex chromosome losses by irradiation of mouse spermatozoa. *Genetics 47*:7-10 (1962).
13. W. P. Spencer and C. Stern. Experiments to test the validity of the linear r-dose/mutation frequency relation in *Drosophila* at low dosage. *Genetics 33*:43-74 (1948).
   E. Caspari and C. Stern. The influence of chronic irradiation with gamma-rays at low dosages on the mutation rate of *Drosophila melanogaster. Genetics 33*:75-95 (1948).
   Delta E. Uphoff and C. Stern. The genetic effects of low intensity irradiation. *Science 109*:609-610 (1949).
14. B. Glass and Rebecca K. Ritterhoff. Mutagenic effect of a 5-r dose of X-rays. *Science 133*:1366 (1961). A preliminary abstract.
15. *The Biological Effects of Atomic Radiation, Summary Reports,* p. 23. National Academy of Sciences—National Research Council, Washington (1956).
16. *Report of the United Nations Committee on the Effects of Atomic Radiation,* p. 41. United Nations, New York (1958).
17. W. L. Russell, Liane B. Russell, and E. M. Kelly. Dependence of mutation rate on radiation intensity. *Intern. J. Radiation Biol.,* Suppl., 311-320. (1960.)
18. W. L. Russell. Effect of radiation dose rate on mutation in mice. *J. Cell Comp. Physiol. 58* (Suppl.): 183-187 (1961).

19. *Health Implications of Fallout from Nuclear Weapons Testing through 1961*. Report No. 3, Federal Radiation Council, Washington (1962).

20. J. V. Neel, in *Biological and Environmental Effects of Nuclear War*, pp. 610-614. Hearings before the Special Subcommittee on Radiation of the Joint Committee on Atomic Energy, Congress of the United States, Eighty-Sixth Congress, June 22-26, 1959. U.S. Govt. Printing Office, Washington (1959).

21. *The Biological Effects of Atomic Radiation, Summary Reports*, p. 11 National Academy of Sciences—National Research Council, Washington (1960).

Appendices

Appendices

Appendix I
A Glossary of Radiation Terminology

SAUL ARONOW, PH.D.

THIS GLOSSARY is intended to aid the general reader who is not expert in medicine or physics in understanding the technical discussions in the book. In planning the articles, it was felt that they would be most valuable if statements were made in precise technical language, reserving explanations of terminology for this appendix. For simplicity the explanations are given in relation to the content of the book. More complete discussions and more extensive glossaries may be found in the references.[1-7]

Absorption—The process by which the energy contained in a particle or ray of radiation is transferred to the target material. The process is complex, but the principle mechanism of energy transfer is *ionization* in the absorber. Ultimately the energy appears as heat.

Absorption Coefficient—The measure of the ability of a given material to absorb or stop radiation. The *linear absorption coefficient* is the stopping power per unit of thickness; dividing by the density gives the *mass absorption coefficient*, or stopping power per unit of mass. The numerical value is a function of the type and energy of the radiation as well as the atomic number and density of the absorber. As a rough rule the stopping power is proportional to the total mass (thickness × density) of the shield and inversely proportional to the energy of the ray. The numerical value is often given in terms of *half-thickness*.

Air Burst—See *Surface Burst.*

Alpha Ray or *Alpha Particle*—See *Radioactive Decay Products.*

Atomic Number—The number of electrons an atom of a particular element has, equal to the net positive charge on the nucleus. It is represented by the letter Z. The atomic number determines the chemical properties, and is the same for all isotopes of the element.

Atomic Weight—The average of the masses of the stable isotopes of a particular element. It is the "weight" used in chemical calculations.

Background Radiation—The level of radiation, varying from place to place, due to diffuse uncontrollable sources of radioactivity. The principal natural sources are *cosmic rays,* from outside the earth, and long-lived radioisotopes, such as radium, potassium-40, etc., that are part of the elements of the earth. A recent addition to the background radiation is man-made fallout. The magnitude of this radiation is shown in Table 1.

Beta Ray—See *Radioactive Decay Products.*

Biological Half-Life—See *Half-Life.*

Blast—The mechanical effect in which the sudden thermal expansion of air around a bomb builds up an enormous pressure, which spreads out as a shock-wave front at velocities greater than that of sound. This is similar to, but infinitely greater than the sonic boom of high-speed aircraft. The *overpressure* or excess of pressure above atmospheric in the wave front, usually tabulated in pounds per square inch (PSI), is a measure of the destructiveness of the blast. The high-pressure wave front is followed by a wave of partial vacuum, which is also destructive.

Cosmic Rays—Streams of radiation consisting of very high-energy heavy particles, for example nuclei of oxygen or iron atoms, that enter the earth's atmosphere from the sun or other reaches of outer space. The atmosphere acts as a shield to reduce the intensity of this radiation, in the process converting part of the energy into secondary radiation such as gamma rays and high-speed electrons.

Curie—The unit of the amount of radioactivity. Originally it referred to 1 gram of radium, but it is now defined as an amount of a radioisotope in which 2.2×10^{12} atoms are disintegrating each minute. See Appendix III for the significance of these large numbers.

Density—An important property of materials used for shielding.

It is the mass of material per unit volume, i.e., pounds per cubic foot. Generally speaking, the greater the density, the better the stopping power. Table 2 lists the densities of some common materials.

Detector—A device for detecting the presence of radiation. It consists of a material that absorbs the energy of the incident radiation, becoming ionized in the process. The ionization in turn is converted to an observable signal, i.e., darkening of a photographic film, an electric pulse in a Geiger-Müller counter, or a light pulse in a scintillation counter.

Dose—The amount of energy absorbed from a stream of radiation by a unit mass of an absorber. For numerical definition, see *Rad*.

Dose Rate—The units discussed under *Rad, Roentgen, REM,* are for the total or integrated dose, independent of the time in which the energy is absorbed. It is frequently important to observe the rate at which the energy is received per unit of time—for example, rads per hour. Such numbers must be examined carefully, for any units of time or of dose may be used. Electronic instruments usually measure dose rate. Dosimeters and film badges usually measure the total accumulated dose.

Ecology—The study of the effect of environment on plant and animals, and of their influence on the environment.

Effective Half-Life—See *Half-Life*.

Electron—An elementary particle of matter having a unit negative charge. Electrons surround the positively charged nucleus of an atom like planets around the sun. However, in radioactive processes, electrons may be emitted from the nucleus with high energy. In this form they are called *Beta Rays*.

Electron-Volt—See *Energy Level*.

Energy Level—Radiation particles are characterized by their type (see *Radioactive Decay Products*) and also by their energy content. The energy is usually expressed in terms of electron volts, ev, or million electron volts, mev. The latter is the energy an electron would acquire if, starting from rest, it were attracted to a positive electrode at a potential of a million volts. In the process of moving over, it would be accelerated to a very high speed and hence would have acquired energy in the form of kinetic energy. With gamma rays, which are not particles, the high energy is associated with high frequency.

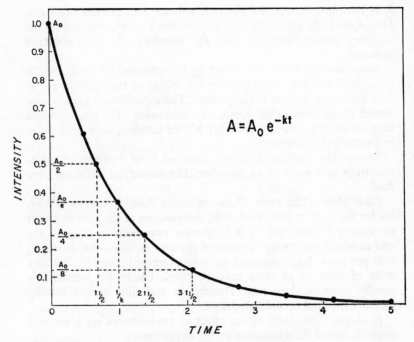

FIGURE 1. *Exponential Decay Function.*
A₀ is the initial value of the function. In each time t½, the amplitude drops by a factor of ½.

Erg—A very small unit of energy. 10^7 ergs per second is 1 watt.

Erythema—An abnormal redness of the skin caused by a variety of agents including ionizing radiation.

Exponential Decay—The mathematical relation shown in Figure 1, $A = A_0e^{-kt}$, where A_0 is the value at zero time and A is the value at time t. Radioactive decay, excretion, attenuation of gamma rays, and many other physical processes follow such a curve. The *half-time* (or *half-thickness*) is the time necessary for A to drop to half its initial value.

Fallout—The radioactive debris that results from a nuclear explosion. This distinguishes nuclear weapons from an equivalent amount of conventional explosives. The amount of fallout depends upon the design of the weapon and the position of the explosion. The fission process itself produces radioisotopes of elements in the middle of the periodic table (listed in Table 1), whereas the

TABLE 1. *Some of the Principal Radioisotopes Produced by the Fission Process*

NUCLIDE	HALF-LIFE	EMISSION	CRITICAL ORGAN
Lanthanum^{140}	1.7 days	Beta; gamma.	Gastrointestinal tract; liver
Molybdenum^{99}	2.8 days	Beta; gamma.	Kidney
Iodine^{131}	8.1 days	Beta; gamma.	Thyroid gland
Barium^{140}	12.8 days	Beta; gamma.	Total body
Praesodymium^{143}	13.7 days	Beta	Bone
Cerium^{141}	33.0 days	Beta; gamma.	Liver
Niobium^{95}	53.0 days	Beta	Bone
Strontium^{89}	35.0 days	Beta; gamma.	Total body
Yttrium^{91}	61.0 days	Beta	Bone
Zirconium^{95}	65.0 days	Beta; gamma.	Total body
Cerium^{144}	282.0 days	Beta; gamma.	Bone
Ruthenium^{106}	1.0 year	Beta	Kidney
Strontium^{90}	28.0 yr.	Beta	Bone
Caesium^{137}	30.0 yr.	Beta; gamma.	Muscle
Carbon^{14}	5568.0 yr.	Beta	Total body
Technetium^{99}	2 x 10^5 yr.	Beta	Kidney
Caesium^{135}	3 x 10^6 yr.	Beta	Muscle
Iodine^{129}	1.7 x 10^7 yr.	Beta; gamma.	Thyroid gland

fusion process does not. In either case the energetic particles released, in particular the neutrons, can activate the atoms of the bomb material as well as earth, air, and other matter near the explosion. A burst near the earth vaporizes this matter, which on condensing collects and carries down the radioactivity. There are three parts to the radiation from a bomb. The first, *immediate radiation,* is not fallout, but radiation generated in the bomb explosion process. The second, *immediate fallout,* is the larger particles that descend to earth near the explosion within minutes or hours. The third, *long-term fallout,* consists of fine particles that are carried into the upper atmosphere and may take days or years to descend.

Fast Neutrons—See Radioactive Decay Products.

Fission—A disintegration process in which the active element is at the heavy end of the periodic table—for example, uranium or plutonium. When the nucleus of one of these elements absorbs an extra neutron, it becomes drastically unbalanced and splits in half, yielding two atoms of elements in the middle of the periodic table. Several neutrons, other radiation, and great thermal energy are also produced in the process. This may be a chain reaction, which once started involves more and more atoms. Hence it is a good basis for a bomb.

TABLE 2. *Characteristics of Materials Required to Reduce
Radiation from Fallout by Half*

MATERIAL	DENSITY lbs./cu. ft.	HALF-THICKNESS ins.
Wood	29	8.8
Water	62.4	4.8
Earth	125	3.3
Concrete	187	2.2
Steel	490	0.7
Lead	710	0.3

Flux—A rate of flow of radiation across a unit area.

Fusion—In this process, isotopes of hydrogen, deuterium (H^2) or tritium (H^3) combine to form helium, again with the release of enormous energy, and neutrons. This process is not self-starting and must be triggered by a fission bomb. When once started it becomes self-sustaining and is theoretically capable of releasing almost unlimited amounts of energy.

Gamma Ray—See *Radioactive Decay Products*.

Half-Life—The time it takes a radioisotope to decrease to half its initial amount of radioactivity. Although the disintegration is a random process, the half-life, as an average value, is fixed for each particular radioisotope. Half-lives range from millionths of a second to thousands of years. Radioactive decay follows an exponential curve as shown in Fig. 1. *Biological half-life* is the time required for half of the amount of an element or chemical compound in the body to be excreted. Many biological processes follow an exponential excretion curve similar to the decay of radioactivity. For a radioisotope, the *effective half-life* is the time for the radioactivity in the body to decrease to half its original value. It is a combination of biological and physical half-lives, stressing the shorter.

Half-Thickness—The thickness of shielding that reduces the intensity of radiation to half its initial value; this applies primarily to gamma radiation which is absorbed exponentially. Some typical values for various materials are given in Table 2. To reduce the intensity by a factor of 1000 requires 10 half-thicknesses of shield (2^{10} equals 1024).

Immediate Radiation—See *Fallout*.

Immediate Fallout—See *Fallout*.

Inverse-Square Law—The intensity of ionizing radiation, like that of any other radiation, decreases inversely as the square of the distance from a point source. This use of distance is one of the most effective means of radiation protection from an isolated source. It should be noted that radiation from a large, uniform plane source falls off with distance with a more complicated formula, more slowly than the inverse square.

Ionizing Radiation—Radiation, either electromagnetic waves or particles, capable of producing ions directly or indirectly in its passage through matter. Ions are electrically charged particles, either electrons stripped from atoms, or molecules with electrons added or subtracted. The chemical reactions that the ions initiate cause the more subtle effects of radiation on biological material. The grosser physical destruction is caused by the enormous amounts of energy in the radiation.

Isotope—One of the several masses that atoms of a particular chemical element may assume. The mass is determined by the sum of neutrons and protons in the nucleus. Some of these combinations are stable; others are unstable, i.e., can not contain all their energy, and on a random basis change to stable combinations by splitting or emitting pieces of matter or bursts of energy. The sum of the protons and neutrons in the nucleus is called the *mass number,* represented by the letter A. A shorthand notation for an isotope is of the form $_zX^A$. For example, a stable isotope of copper, mass number 63, atomic number 29 is $_{29}Cu^{63}$. Usually the atomic number is not stated and the particular isotope is represented by its mass number, i.e., Cu-63. These unstable isotopes are called *radioisotopes*. A more precise designation is *radionuclide,* which emphasizes the point that the properties of the nucleus determine stability.

Linear Energy Transfer—Or *LET,* is a property of radiation that is closely related to the *Relative Biological Efficiency, RBE.* It is the space rate at which the particle loses energy as it moves through the absorbing medium. A large charged particle, such as an alpha particle, interacts much more vigorously with the atoms of the absorber than a highly penetrating gamma ray of the same energy. The alpha moves only a short distance before its energy is all absorbed and it stops, so that there is a high rate of energy transfer per unit length of travel. Since the biological effects depend on energy absorption, the higher the LET, the greater the RBE in the particular region of absorption.

LD_{50}—The 50 per cent lethal dose is the level of radiation dose at which half the exposed population will die. It is used as a criterion of dangerous dose levels. Other values, LD_{20} or LD_{80}, at which 20 and 80 per cent respectively would die, are also used. Since this is a statistical value dependent on the type of organism, state of health of the population, type of radiation, exposure pattern, and so forth, it should be used only as an order of magnitude, not as a certain number. Table 1 of Appendix III lists the biological significance of a number of radiation levels. These are largely approximate values, or estimates based on scanty knowledge.

Long-Term Fallout—See *Fallout*.

Mass—The amount of actual matter that a piece of substance contains.

Mass-Energy Relation—The basic physical principle from which the enormous energy of nuclear explosions derives is the Einstein relation $E = mc^2$, which equates changes in energy with changes in mass. The magnitudes and significance are discussed in Appendix III. It implies that, contrary to the classical concepts of the conservation of mass and the conservation of energy, it is the sum of mass plus energy that is conserved.

Mass Number—See *Isotope*.

Mev—See *Energy Levels*.

Natural Radiation—There is a certain amount of very long-lived radioactivity present in the natural elements that exist on the earth. For example, radium in granite, uranium in clays, a radioactive isotope of potassium, K-40, in all living matter, etc. In addition, cosmic rays shower the earth with very high energy radiation and also activate atoms in the atmosphere and on the earth to produce shorter-lived radioisotopes. The level of this natural radiation is low and apparently not harmful.

Neutron—The elementary particle which together with the proton are the building blocks that make up the nuclei of atoms. It is a particle that has essentially the same mass as the proton but has no electrical charge.

Neutron Activation—Neutrons interact with matter by being absorbed in the nucleus of an atom. This changes the structure of the nucleus and usually results in an unstable configuration. For example, normal, stable, copper[63] absorbs a thermal neutron and becomes radioactive copper[64]. In the process, the total mass decreases slightly, the difference appearing as a high-energy gamma ray. Neutron activation may be used for trace-metal analysis, for bomb detonation, or for producing useful radioisotopes in a reactor.

Nucleus—The positively charged center of an atom, around which are the orbital electrons. The nucleus consists of protons and neutrons tightly packed together by the action of poorly understood very powerful short-range forces. Only certain combinations of protons and neutrons are stable. See *Isotope*.

Nuclear Radiation—The energy released or radiated when an unstable nucleus adjusts itself to a more stable state.

Nuclide—See *Isotope*.

Overpressure—See *Blast*.

Particles of Radiation—Many types of radiation are actually particles—electrons, neutrons, atomic nuclei, etc.—rather than electromagnetic waves like radio, light, or gamma rays. Their high energy results from moving at speeds approaching the speed of light, enabling them to interact with atoms in their paths.

Photon—All electromagnetic-wave radiation—light, x-rays, or gamma rays, travels at the speed of light in the form of discrete bundles of energy called photons. The amount of energy in each of these units is proportional to the frequency of the wave. The fact that the energy is emitted in discrete units makes the wave radiation have properties of a particle.

Positron—An elementary particle of matter, having the same mass as an electron, but having a positive charge. It is formed during nuclear disintegration or from the energy of a high-energy gamma ray. The positron is unstable and disappears by reacting with an electron, converting their masses into two photons of gamma energy.

PSI—Or pounds per square inch, a unit of pressure. See *Blast*.

Proton—An elementary particle of matter, a building block of the nucleus, having the same mass as a neutron but a unit positive charge. The mass of a proton is 1860 times greater than that of an electron.

Protection Factor—This composite factor, depending on distance, shielding materials, and type of radiation, describes how much a given shelter will reduce the dose rate from that existing outside. The range of values is about 2 for the first floor, 10 for the basement of a frame house, 250 for a basement shelter of the type recommended by the Office of Civilian Defense Mobilization to 1000 for an elaborate earth-concrete shelter.

Quantum—A fundamental unit of energy, in steps of which

energy is transferred during interactions. Since electromagnetic energy travels in discrete units, photons are often called quanta.

Rad—A unit of absorbed energy, or dose, applicable to all types of radiations. It is defined as the absorption of 100 ergs of energy per gram of absorbing matter. For gamma rays of moderate energy the rad and roentgen are approximately equal, and the two terms are often loosely interchanged.

Radiation—In general, any process in which energy is transmitted across space without direct contact. It originally signified electromagnetic wave radiation, heat, or light, etc., but has been extended to include high-energy-particle radiation.

Radioactive Decay Products—The "radiation" that results from a nuclear disintegration may be a combination of several types, each having a characteristic mass, electrical charge, and energy. *Gamma rays* are photons of electromagnetic energy, like light or x-rays, but of higher energy; they have neither mass nor charge. *Beta rays* are electrons, with positive or negative charge, moving at very high speeds. *Alpha rays* are positively charged helium nuclei, again moving at high speeds. Excess *neutrons* may be ejected from a nucleus. They are called *thermal neutrons* at very low speed and *fast neutrons* at high speeds. Neutrons have mass but no charge. When heavy nuclei break apart as in fission, the pieces may be nuclei of other atoms. If these have high speeds they are also considered to be radiation. These *fission products* are themselves usually radioisotopes and undergo further radioactive decay.

Radioisotope—See *Isotope*.

Relative Biological Efficiency—Or RBE, for a given type and energy of radiation, is the dose of gamma rays necessary to produce the same biological effect as a unit dose of the radiation in question. Thus, REM = RBE × RAD, if *REM* is in *rads*. The RBE is a function not only of the type of radiation and its energy but also of the biological test that is used as a criterion. Thus, a value of RBE calculated from a survival test on dry yeast may be greatly different from the values obtained for leukemia induction in man. The RBE is roughly 1 for beta rays, 5 for thermal neutrons, 10 for fast neutrons, and 20 for alpha particles.

REM—The *roentgen-equivalent* (*man*) is the quantity of a particular type and energy of radiation which, when absorbed in man, produces the same effect as the absorption of 1 roentgen of gamma rays. The expression may also be used in terms of rads rather than roentgens. In a mixed radiation flux the total REM is the sum of the value for each species.

Roentgen—The fundamental unit of the quantity of gamma radiation or x-radiation. It is measured by the ionization, as a quantity of electricity, produced in a standard volume of air by the flux of radiation. It depends on the product of the number of photons in the flux and their energy.

Shielding—A layer of matter, usually of dense materials like earth or lead, placed between a source of radioactivity and a target, to absorb the radiation and hence reduce the amount reaching the target. The properties of some shielding materials are given in Table 2.

Stopping Power—A measure of the ability of a particular material to act as a shield against a given radiation.

Surface Burst—An explosion of a bomb at the surface of the earth. This produces maximum fallout at the expense of blast and thermal damage. An *air burst* above the surface, where the fireball barely touches the earth, has minimum fallout but increased blast and thermal effect.

Thermal Neutron—A free neutron that has been slowed down to thermal equilibrium with the atoms in its vicinity. Because it has no charge it can readily enter the nucleus of one of these atoms. See *Neutron Activation*.

Thermal Radiation—The radiation of energy in the form of heat or infrared electromagnetic waves. Although the energy per *photon* is very much less than that of gamma rays, the total amount of thermal radiation in the case of bomb burst may be enormous.

Whole-Body Irradiation—The process of subjecting the entire biological organism to nuclear radiation. This produces more serious damage than does local irradiation of a limited part of the organism.

X-Ray—Radiation of electromagnetic energy similar to but usually at a lower energy level than gamma rays. X-rays are usually produced by machines rather than by radioactive decay.

Yield—The explosive power of a bomb is expressed in terms of the number of tons of TNT that would have the same explosive effect. This is of the order of thousands of tons, KT, or millions, MT. Fission bombs are physically limited in size and hence in yield, but fusion bombs can, in principle, be made as large as desired. A ton of TNT is equivalent to 10^9 calories.

References

1. *Radiation Dosimetry*. Edited by G. J. Hine and G. L. Brownell. 932 pp. New York: Academic Press, 1956.
2. United States Armed Forces Special Weapons Project. *The Effects of Nuclear Weapons*. Edited by S. Glasstone. 579 pp. Washington, D. C.: Government Printing Office, 1957. (Pamphlet 39-3.)
3. United States Atomic Energy Commission. *General Handbook for Radiation Monitoring*. Edited by J. E. Dommer. Third Edition. 180 pp. Washington, D. C.: Government Printing Office, 1958. (LA-1835.)
4. United States Congress, Joint Committee on Atomic Energy. *Fallout from Nuclear Weapons Tests: Summary-analysis of Hearings, May, 1959.*
5. United States Congress, Joint Committee on Atomic Energy. *Biological and Environmental Effects of Nuclear War: Summary-analysis of Hearings, June 22-26, 1959*. 58 pp. Washington, D. C.: Government Printing Office, 1959.
6. Great Britain, Medical Research Council. *The Hazards to Man of Nuclear and Allied Radiation: Presented to Lord President of Council to Parliament by command of Her Majesty, June 1956*. London: Her Majesty's Stationery Office, 1956. (Command Paper 9780.) Supp. 1960.
7. *Radioecology*. Edited by V. Schultz and A. W. Klement, Jr. (Reinhold, New York) (In press.)

Appendix II
A Glossary of Medical Terms

AGORAPHOBIA—Fear of open spaces

ANOREXIA—Loss of appetite for food

ATAXIA—Muscular incoordination

CORTISONE—A hormone administered for several diseases—often necessary for life

DIGITALIS—A drug used in the treatment of heart disease

DIABETES MELLITUS—Ordinary diabetes

DYSCRASIA (as in blood dyscrasia)—An abnormal state (of the blood)

EPILATION—Loss of hair

EQUINE ENCEPHALITIS—A disease involving convulsions and coma, transmitted by mosquitoes

ESCHERICHIA COLI—Common intestinal bacteria, usually harmless

FIBROSIS—The formation of scar tissue

GRANULOCYTES—A type of infection-fighting blood cell

GRANULOCYTOPENIA—A deficiency of granulocytes

HEMATOLOGIC (DEPRESSION)—Deficiencies in blood cells causing abnormal symptoms

HEMATOPOIETIC—Pertaining to the formation of blood cells

HEPATITIS—A liver disease

HYPOVOLEMIA—Loss of blood or plasma

HYPOXIA—A deficiency of oxygen

INSULIN—A hormone required daily by some diabetics—often essential to life

LYMPHOCYTES—A variety of white blood cells (leukocytes) which fights infection

METASTATIC—The transfer of disease from one part to another not directly connected with it

MICROCEPHALY—Abnormal smallness of the head

MORPHOLOGICALLY NECROTIC—Unable to form functioning structures or organs

MUCOSA—A mucous membrane, producer of mucous

NECROSIS—Death of tissue which is in contact with living tissue

NEONATAL—Pertaining to the first four weeks of a baby's life

NEOPLASIA—The formation of tumors

NEUTROPHILS—A variety of blood cells which fights infection

PLATELETS—Blood cell concerned in the coagulation of the blood

PNEUMONITIS—Infection of the lung

PURPURA—A skin discoloraton caused by bleeding under the skin

RUBELLA—German measles

SEQUELAE—Lesion or affliction caused by or following an attack of a disease

SYNDROME—A set of symptoms which occur together

THROMBOCYTOPENIA—A deficiency of platelets

TRIAGE—The sorting out of wounded persons

TRIMESTER—Three months (usually of pregnancy)

Appendix III
Orders of Magnitude

Saul Aronow, Ph.D.

One of the many factors that add confusion to the analysis of the nuclear bomb problem is the range of numerical magnitudes that must be considered. In these brief comments we shall try to explain some of the mental gyrations one must go through to relate even qualitatively the gamut of phenomena that make up the nuclear problem.

It is simply very difficult to comprehend the significance of the range of these numbers. This difficulty is a conceptual problem that is the root of many of the contradictory statements in the published evaluations of the hazards of nuclear radiation.

In ordinary life we know what are large and small quantities in a particular class of objects. We can appreciate a range of numbers from 1 to 1,000,000 whether this is dollars in a budget, people in a city, or cells in an organ. But somewhere above this our experience fails and our intuitive grasp of magnitude is lost. For scientific work, however, much larger numbers are needed, and we learn how to write such numbers even if we do not fully comprehend them. The compact mathematical notation of powers of 10 may be used. For example $1,000,000 = 10^6$ and $.000001 = 10^{-6}$. A number such as 10^{100}, 1 followed by 100 zeros, is a number larger than all the particles in the entire universe. It may be easily written, but it has very little comprehensibility. You probably do not believe this because the notation is deceivingly simple. Play with it a little, and see how rapidly the quantities get completely out of control for a few changes in the power of 10.

In nuclear phenomena just such numbers are dealt with. Events occurring in a single electron may be measured, or, at the other extreme, forces of sizes previously observed only in cosmic events may be generated. In this enormous gamut of numbers it is easy vastly to overrate or underrate hazards by sliding a few powers of 10 up or down. This may be illustrated by specific examples with numbers.

Certain radioactive isotopes emit positrons, or positive electrons, when they disintegrate. A free positron interacts with a negative electron so that they both disappear as matter and are transformed into energy, in the form of two gamma rays. The amount of this energy may be calculated by means of the Einstein mass-energy relation $E = mc^2$. The velocity of light is $c = 3 \times 10^{10}$ centimeters per second, and the mass, m, of a single electron is 9×10^{-28} gram, so that the corresponding energy is 8×10^{-7} ergs, or, expressed in electron volts, 500,000 ev. A single such interaction can be detected with great certainty because these high-energy gamma rays may be considered to have a large information content per photon. That is to say, if the energy of one of these gamma rays is absorbed by ionizing the molecules of a suitable detector, about 20,000 ion pairs are formed. This large number of ions appearing at the same time in a small space may be observed by a variety of instruments. Although in this sense, information-carrying capacity, the energy per gamma ray is large, it is very small in terms of ordinary energy levels. It would require 10^{15} of these per second, or the equivalent of 30,000 curies of radioactivity to light a 100-watt electric bulb.

This low total energy but high energy density is of particular significance in biologic effects because biologic materials are very highly organized chemical systems, many of which are primarily designed for information transmission. Twenty thousand ion pairs may cause an appreciable destruction in such information centers as a cell nucleus.

The biological hazard of radiation derives from this high specific destructiveness of individual particles of radiation to biological materials. Again, as part of the uncertainty of these numbers, it must be appreciated that there is an extremely low probability that if a ray is absorbed in the body it will affect any critical molecules.

Even if it does destroy some critical molecules, the organism usually has many to spare. Unfortunately, although the probability of the occurrence of this chain of events is low, it is not known exactly how low. Human beings exist in a sea of background radiation that apparently does them little harm, but how much above background the radiation need go to have a greater effect is not known with any degree of certainty.

The probability that lung cancer will develop in a person smoking 20 cigarettes a day is much greater than the probability that leukemia will develop from exposure to 20 mr a day, and yet the latter causes much more public concern. Two reasons for this are the aura of mystery surrounding radiation and the fact that the *low numbers* of background radiation are mentally associated with the *high numbers* of bomb levels. The unfortunate fact that official statements have seemed to reverse the process, belittling the effects of bombs by identifying them with background levels, has only added to the public misunderstanding and uneasiness.

What happens to the numbers which are related to bombs? The mass of an electron is equivalent in energy to 8×10^{-14} watt seconds, but 1 gram of mass would contain 1.1×10^{27} electrons, equivalent to 9×10^{13} watt seconds. This is an incomprehensibly large amount of energy, equivalent to exploding 20,000 tons of TNT.

Thus, in discussing energy levels between background radiation and 10-megaton bombs, a ratio of about 1 to 10^{30} must be examined. With the very delicate balance of physical and chemical conditions under which life exists, it is not surprising that there is anxiety in the minds of the public and the scientific community about how sure supposedly safe levels are.

Actually, of course, numbers can be assigned with a fair degree of precision to many levels of this energy range. The physical properties of matter, in particular, may be accurately measured. Unfortunately, the biological effects of radiation are poorly understood and imperfectly measured. Is a level of 100 rads a hazard? Not in military terms, since it is not immediately lethal. Yet by peacetime standards, 0.1 rad is considered a high dose for a radiation worker.

Some reasonable values for biological effects of radiation are given in Table 1 at the end of this Appendix. These values are largely approximate: some are estimates based on scanty information, and almost all are statistical averages that apply only on a

TABLE 1. Biological Effects of Radiation*

PART OF BODY IRRADIATED	DURATION OF EXPOSURE	DESCRIPTION SOURCE OF RADIATION	POPULATION IRRADIATED	DOSE RATE r/wk.	TOTAL DOSE REM	EFFECT (OR ACCEPTED STANDARD)
Whole body	Long term	Cosmic rays at sea level	Entire population	0.001		None detectable
		Fallout from bomb tests	Entire population	0.001		None detectable
		Natural background	Entire population	0.002–0.005		None detectable
		Any source	Entire population	0.01		(Maximum permissible for general population)
		Any source	Entire population	0.02	50	Statistical life-span shortening
		Any source	Workers over age 18	0.1		(Maximum permissible for radiation workers)
		Any source	Individual	0.3		None detectable
		Any source	Individual	7.0		Leukopenia
		Any source	Individual	50.0		Carcinogenesis
Whole body	Single dose	Any source	Fetus in utero		2–4	Doubling of childhood cancer
		Any source	Individual		25	Blood-cell changes
		Any source	Individual		50	Marginal radiation sickness
		Any source	Individual		150	Recoverable radiation sickness
		Any source	Individual		200	Marginal radiation death
		Any source	Individual		450	LD_{50} in man
		Any source	Individual		900	LD_{100} in man
Gonads	Long term (30 years)	Any source	Entire population age 30	0.04	60	Estimated doubling of mutation rate
Hands	Long term	Any source	Individual	1.5		None detectable
Bone	Long term (20 years)	Radium in bone	Individual	5.0		Marginal bone-tumor induction
Local	Single dose	Chest X-ray examination	Individual		0.02–0.2	None detectable
Local	Single dose	G.I. Series (X-ray exam)	Individual		10–30	None detectable
Local	Single dose	X-ray exam of teeth	Individual		1.5–100	None detectable
Local	Single dose	Fluoroscopy	Individual		5–250	None detectable

Thyroid gland	Single dose	Any source	Children	Marginal cancer induction	200
Skin	Single dose	Any source	Individual	Hair loss	300
Ovaries	Single dose	Any source	Individual	Sterility	300
Testes	Single dose	Any source	Individual	Sterility	500
Skin	Single dose	Any source	Individual	Erythema	300–1000
Eyes	Single dose	Any source	Individual	Cataracts	1500
Skin	Single dose	Any source	Individual	Marginal cancer induction	2000
Tumor	Single dose	Any source	Individual	Lethal to tumor	6000
Insects	Single dose	Any source		Lethal to insects	10^3 to 10^4
Bacteria	Single dose	Any source		Lethal to bacteria	10^4 to 5×10^5
Viruses	Single dose	Any source		Lethal to viruses	10^5 to 5×10^7
Plastics	Single dose	Any source		Radiation polymerization	2×10^8

* It should be noted that these values are largely approximate, or estimates based on scanty information.

probabalistic basis. However, they do show clearly the contradictory aspects of the biological problem. There are wide ranges of dosage where harmful effects are arguable, other ranges where a small change may be lethal.

The long-range ecological and social significance of nuclear warfare is even more poorly understood and evaluated. Effects can be estimated only in terms of orders of magnitude.

An evaluation of the medical problems of nuclear warfare must therefore be made with this unfamiliar and approximate frame of reference in mind. There are two extreme views. Those who stress the long-term effects of low levels of radiation may rightly be criticized as worrying about dangers that are real but minor in the face of national security. On the other hand, those who are employed in civil defense and optimistically claim to be able to save x per cent of the population, should know that the military potential exists, even at present, to destroy civilization completely if not all human existence. A sane approach must recognize that both extremes are right and wrong. It is the responsibility of each of us to learn something of this life and death numbers game so that we can weigh the validity of the statements we are presented with on the basis of criteria of necessity and danger.

Appendix IV
Casualty Data for Selected Cities

	Baltimore	Boston	Chicago	Cleveland	Detroit	Los Angeles
Population* (1000's)	1338	2875	5498	1466	3017	4367
Number killed first day (1000's)	591	1052	545	394	820	698
Number fatally injured (1000's)	466	1084	447	298	593	2136
Number surviving injured (1000's)	174	467	648	316	557	814
Total casualties surviving first day (1000's)	640	1551	1095	614	1150	2950
Number of physicians†	2970	6560	9400	3070	5130	12,340
Number killed first day	1310	2380	930	830	1400	1970
Number fatally injured	1030	2470	760	620	1010	6030
Number surviving injured	390	1070	1110	660	950	2300
Number uninjured	240	640	6600	960	1770	2040
Estimated number of practicing physicians‡	340	910	6880	1130	2010	2620
Casualties per practicing physician§	1880	1700	160	540	570	1130

	N.Y.C.	Philadelphia	Pittsburgh	St. Louis	San Fran.	Wash., D.C.
Population* (1000's)	12,904	3671	2214	1292	2241	1465
Number killed first day (1000's)	3464	1309	597	563	734	597
Number fatally injured (1000's)	2634	989	659	370	769	433
Number surviving injured (1000's)	2278	777	43	161	301	228
Total casualties surviving first day (1000's)	4912	1766	702	531	1070	661
Number of physicians†	23,750	8110	3000	3020	6130	4330
Number killed first day	6370	2900	810	1320	2010	1710
Number fatally injured	4850	2180	890	890	2100	1280
Number surviving injured	4200	1720	60	380	820	680
Number uninjured	8330	1310	1240	430	1200	660
Estimated number of practicing physicians‡	9380	1740	1255	530	1410	830
Casualties per practicing physician§	520	1010	560	1000	760	800

* 1950 population figures.
† Includes M.D.'s and D.O.'s, including those employed by the U.S. Public Health Service and the Veterans Administration, but not by the Armed Forces (1959 figures).
‡ Includes 25% of the nonfatally injured physicians.
§ Total casualties surviving first day divided by estimated number of practicing physicians.

The data in this appendix are taken directly from two sources: (1) The casualty estimates for the population as a whole were presented in the Hearings on the Biological and Environmental Effects of Nuclear War before the Special Subcommittee on Radiation of the Joint Committee on Atomic Energy of the Congress of the United States in June, 1959. (2) The physician population data were prepared by the Department of Health, Education, and Welfare and appeared in Health Manpower Source Book Number 10 issued by the Government Printing Office in 1960.

The casualty estimates for the total population were based on the 1950 census; these were not increased proportionately to the growth in population since 1950. The casualty estimates therefore represent an underestimate of the number of casualties to be expected from an attack of this pattern in the 1960's or later.

The physician population data are for the year 1959, the latest data available to us. The total, as reported earlier, "includes physicians of all ages, and many in at least partial retirement. This calculation also counts, as physicians available for post-attack service, many whose work has centered on administration, laboratory research, or preclinical teaching rather than on clinical care of patients. Additionally, it must be remembered that this count of functioning physicians includes pathologists, psychiatrists, and other specialists who have had little recent training or experience in the treatment of burns, trauma, or radiation injury." Furthermore, although the risk for physicians is clearly higher than for the general population (see p. 24), we have made the conservative assumption that physicians are at the same risk as the population as a whole. We have further assumed that 25 per cent of the nonfatally injured physicians would be able and willing to continue practicing after the attack. Therefore, the number of "Practicing Physicians" given in the tables represents a serious *overestimate* of the number of physicians available for service in the postattack period.

The underestimation of the number of casualties and the overestimation of the number of physicians means that the estimate of the number of casualties per practicing physician given in the last line of the tables is a minimum figure. The consequences of these ratios may be made clear by a few examples. If every physician in Los Angeles were to spend an average of only ten minutes on diagnosis and treatment of each injured patient (including the time needed to get from patient to patient) and were willing and able to work for twenty hours a day, it would require nine days before every injured person could be seen for the first time. If every physician in the District of Columbia spent only an average of 10 minutes per patient and worked solidly 20 hours a day, it would require 7 days before every injured person were seen. It follows that most of the injured persons will never see a physician, even for the simple administration of narcotics, before they die.

Contributors

SAUL ARONOW, Ph.D. Research associate in medicine, Harvard Medical School; Assistant physicist, Department of Medicine, Massachusetts General Hospital.

NICHOLAS C. AVERY, M.D. Teaching fellow in psychiatry, Harvard Medical School; Chief resident in psychiatry, Massachusetts Mental Health Center.

ROBERT COLMAN, M.D. Clinical associate, National Heart Institute, Bethesda, Maryland.

FRANK R. ERVIN, M.D. Assistant professor of psychiatry, Harvard Medical School; Psychiatrist, Massachusetts General Hospital.

H. JACK GEIGER, M.D., M. Sci. Hyg. (Epidem.) Assistant resident in medicine, II (Harvard) Medical Service, Boston City Hospital.

BENTLEY GLASS, Ph.D. Professor of Biology, The Johns Hopkins University.

JON B. GLAZIER, M.D. Research fellow in medicine, Harvard Medical School.

CAVIN P. LEEMAN, M.D. Teaching fellow in psychiatry, Harvard Medical School; Resident in psychiatry, Beth Israel Hospital, Boston.

P. HERBERT LEIDERMAN, M.D. Associate in psychiatry, Harvard Medical School; Psychiatrist, Massachusetts Mental Health Center.

BERNARD LOWN, M.D. Assistant professor of medicine, Department of Nutrition, Harvard School of Public Health.

JACK H. MENDELSON, M.D. Associate in psychiatry, Harvard Medical School; Assistant psychiatrist, Massachusetts General Hospital.

DAVID NATHAN, M.D. Research associate in medicine, Harvard Medical School; Junior associate in medicine, Peter Bent Brigham Hospital, Boston.

GERARD PIEL. Publisher of *Scientific American*.

STEPHEN SHOHET, M.D. Clinical associate, National Cancer Institute, Bethesda, Maryland.

VICTOR W. SIDEL, M.D. Instructor in biophysics, Harvard Medical School; Assistant in medicine, Peter Bent Brigham Hospital, Boston.